Advance Praise for
Trail to Redemption

"My advice to writers is always 'Let the pictures tell the story,' and in Richard Stevens's *Trail to Redemption*, the 'pictures' are vivid, unforgettable, and go straight to the heart. The woman he calls 'the Vietnamese Annie Oakley,' Hoang Thi Nu, is a superhero for our times. Her life, as it becomes entwined with her 'enemy' (Stevens), is like no other story. Read this book: You will see love and war in a new light."

— David F. Oyster, Documentary Filmmaker; *Cosmos* (Carl Sagan), *The Astronomers*

"Move over *Apocalypse Now*! Richard Stevens's memoir is powerful, moving, and rare amongst the primarily macho accounts of the Vietnam War. A US Foreign Service Officer during the Vietnam War and adviser to an elite unit of ex-VC guérillas, Stevens describes his struggle to retain his humanity in the midst of a terrible conflict. He develops understanding and respect for the bravery of the enemy, and especially for Hoàng Thi Nu, a young woman Việt Cong being tracked by his unit. But his attempt to lessen her suffering when she is captured backfires and she finds herself in even worse conditions of detention and subjected to torture. By telling his story, Stevens courageously bears witness to the forgotten and shameful history of US torture during the Vietnam War."

— Sherry Buchanan, author of *On the Ho Chi Minh Trail: The Blood Road, The Women Who Defended It, The Legacy*

"The *Trail to Redemption* is an unforgettable memoir that traces Richard L. Stevens's journey from war to peace in Vietnam. Stevens, despite his civilian status, becomes an active participant, and his adventuresome spirit leads him to nearly kill the person he comes to most admire, and even loves—Hoang Thi Nu, aka the Vietnamese Annie Oakley. He and his comrades capture her and carry her into captivity as one would carry a slain tiger suspended from a pole. Stevens, who works side by side with Vietnamese personnel who purportedly support the US presence in Vietnam, is immersed in a shadowy world of double agents whose loyalty and intentions are always in doubt. Stevens navigates uncertainty with a deep empathy for the Vietnamese."

—James Janko, author of *What We Don't Talk About* and
Buffalo Boy and Geronimo

"This is a well-written, even poetic memoir by a young American advisor during the Vietnam War. It is a fast-paced, real-life adventure story that captures the frenzied and fearful flavor of a war in which it was difficult to know who was on your side and who was the enemy. Above all, it is a story of personal courage, respect and love in a time of war. This book provided the perspective of a principled contemporary who enthusiastically sought out the adventure of war and embraced it. It is a book of many surprises."

—David Krieger, President emeritus of the Nuclear Age Peace
Foundation and author of many books

"Richard Stevens became one of the few Americans to ever penetrate into that Asian Heart of Darkness—the Ho Chi Minh Trail. That almost impossible feat became an even more improbable pursuit of war and love in this remarkable personal story. Like Stevens himself, it is a life and a Vietnamese encounter that is one of a kind."
— Bill McWhirter, correspondent for TIME and LIFE in Vietnam and winner of several major journalism awards

"Few Americans know Vietnam—the war and its toll, the people and their beauty—as Richard Stevens does. Since 1965, Stevens has charted some of the least known corners of Vietnam, and now, returning to that tortured land, and his own past, Stevens brings a keen emotional intelligence to tell the story of the 'Vietnamese Annie Oakley'—a woman he knew and, thankfully for 21st century readers, in Trail to Redemption has brought back to life."
— Andrew Meier, Associate Professor of Writing at The New School in New York, and author of *Black Earth: A Journey Through Russia After the Fall*, which was nominated for a Pulitzer Prize

TRAIL TO REDEMPTION

Love and War in Vietnam

Richard L. Stevens

Trail to Redemption

Richard L. Stevens

ISBN-13: 978-988-8769-67-4

Cover art by Wailehua Gray

BIOGRAPHY & AUTOBIOGRAPHY

EB173

Published by Earnshaw Books Ltd. (Hong Kong)

DEDICATION

To Hoàng Thị Nữ, "the Vietnamese Annie Oakley"

In War, in the Ancient Tradition of Vietnamese
Women Warriors
In Peace, Humanitarian and Herald of Love and
Forgiveness

Also by Richard L. Stevens

Organic Gardening in Hawaii, (Petroglyph Press, 1981)

The Trail: A History of the Ho Chi Minh Trail and the Role of Nature in the War in Vietnam (Garland Publishing, 1993)

Mission on the Ho Chi Minh Trail: Nature, Myth, and War in Vietnam (University of Oklahoma Press, 1995)

Tropical Organic Gardening Hawaiian Style (Petroglyph Press, 2003)

"Meeting with the Goddess: True Story of the Vietnamese Annie Oakley" in *Veterans of War, Veterans of Peace*, Edited by Maxine Hong Kingston (Chiron Publications, 2006)

PREFACE

Seeking power, I found redemption.
— Anonymous

LIKE MY COUNTRY, I paid my own way to the war. In 1965, when the big U.S. buildup began, I was teaching in Japan, and I went to the Vietnamese Embassy in Tokyo and applied for a tourist visa.

"You want to visit my country. Why?"

"I've heard it's very beautiful. I'm also interested in its culture."

"What do you know about our culture?"

"Not much. I want to learn."

"I can only issue you a visa if you have a ticket to leave. Fill out this form and come back."

I was on fire to get to Vietnam. I had been in the Marines twice without finding "the big test" I was yearning for. I had graduated from college in U.S. History, attended graduate school in International Relations, and traveled around Asia, but I still wasn't sure of my role in the world. Something powerful was stirring in me, though, calling me to Vietnam, where some of my buddies from my Marine Corps days were now experiencing their first combat. I bought a ticket to Bangkok on a French ship that also stopped in Saigon and went back to the Vietnamese Embassy.

"Two weeks!" the visa officer said, and he slammed a big black stamp in my passport. "And make sure you're on that next boat to Bangkok."

Over the next six years, I was in and out of Vietnam many times. I got a job as a refugee advisor, was a civil affairs liaison with U.S. Marine, Army, Air Force, and Navy units, and worked in rural development, all parts of the "Hearts and Minds" program to win the allegiance of Vietnamese to the U.S.-supported Saigon government and away from the Communist Việt Cộng guerrillas.

By the hot summer of 1969, I was a U.S. Foreign Service Officer and the advisor to an elite unit of ex- Việt Cộng guerrillas and former North Vietnamese Army soldiers operating in Quảng Trị, the northernmost province in South Vietnam. These ex-enemy, an "Armed Propaganda Team (APT)," were part of the Chiêu Hội, or "Open Arms" program to persuade communist fighters to defect, or "rally," and then use them and the valuable intelligence and weapons they brought against their former comrades. The communists detested Chiêu Hội and frequently penetrated it with "false ralliers," and while the APT had a high *esprit de corps*, there were also healthy doses of suspicion and fatalism, which I, as the lone American, shared. And even though I had many "brothers in arms" relationships, I knew that many of my "brothers" could still be VC.

Chapter 1's title, "Meeting with the Goddess," is from Joseph Campbell's classic study of comparative myths, *The Hero with a Thousand Faces*, in which the hero's journey found in myths and religions around the world is understood to be the life-journey of us all. This book is a chronicle of my own epic journey. I have changed some of the names.

1

MEETING WITH THE GODDESS

> VERY HUMBLY, let me introduce to you the Vietnamese
> woman, whom beloved Uncle Hồ has called "heroic,
> courageous, loyal, and defiant." Inherited from
> heroic blood of the Trưng sisters and Lady Triệu, the
> Vietnamese women consider fighting against foreign
> invasion natural and normal…to me, my courage and
> loyalty are just part of being a Vietnamese woman.
>
> —Hoàng Thị Nữ

IT'S ALREADY hot at 8 a.m. as I leave my guarded compound in
Quảng Trị City and head for the Chiêu Hội Center. The empty
road ahead bakes on a Vietnamese holiday, something about
"Wandering Souls." My counterpart, the South Vietnamese
government official I advise, is staying home with his wife
and two little girls. I had nothing better to do, I was longing
for adventure, and I wanted to practice Vietnamese with the
ex-guerrillas guarding the Center. They, as "ralliers" to the
South Vietnamese and U.S. side, and "traitors" to their former
comrades, got no holiday from threat of attack to their sandbag
fort on the edge of town.

I ease my Scout down my narrow driveway. The wrinkled
old Vietnamese veteran who guards the front of my house comes
out of his sandbag bunker and drags open the iron and barbed-
wire gate, gouging a trench in the dirt. I turn east toward the sea.

Behind me, the hot dry wind that blows all summer from Laos sweeps past, stirring dead leaves at the side of the road.

I parallel the river, then swing south past the broad, mossy moat and high stone walls of Quảng Trị Citadel, ancient feudal castle now with M-60 machine guns mounted in the arrow slits, and the yellow and red flag of South Vietnam flying in the hot wind. At a narrow, bamboo- framed dirt lane I turn left and bump along between thatched houses and packed-earth rice- drying yards, the bamboo reaching, scraping my Scout. I growl along in low, dropping into holes cut by winter rains, dust bowls now in summer heat. Chickens scratch, low-slung pigs root, women in conical hats pass rocking with carrying poles and big tins full of sloshing water.

Gun towers rise ahead, and I pass through the barbed-wire gate of the Chiêu Hội Center, the ralliers' fortress-island at the edge of the rice-paddy sea. The guard, an ex-Việt Cộng guerrilla with a Chinese-made AK-47 slung across his back, calls, "*Ông cố vấn!* Mr. Advisor! Working on the 'Wandering Souls' holiday?"

I wonder what "Wandering Souls" is about as I cross the dusty compound and park outside my tin-roofed office. Suddenly, a motor scooter zooms through the gate, and Ông Ba, "Mr. Three," one of our district agents, pulls up in a cloud of smoke and dust. Ba, whom I don't like and definitely don't trust, breathes stale black tobacco smell and rancid *nước mắm* fish sauce directly into my face and says in Vietnamese, "We have to talk, cố vấn. Call Đặng Sỹ. Very important!"

Đặng Sỹ, Commander of the Chiêu Hội Armed Propaganda Team, 105 ex-VC guerrillas and North Vietnamese soldiers, comes in wearing dark sunglasses, tailored Marine camouflage, brown beret, and .45 pistol hanging to his knee. Tall, slim, and super-intelligent, Đặng Sỹ is a former VC schoolteacher. He looks at Ba with distaste. Besides smelling bad, Ba is a South Vietnamese

4

government official, *not* an ex-VC.

Ba sits in my chair, lights up a Gauloise, and fills the room with tobacco smoke and foul breath. Đặng Sỹ stays at the door. I lean by the open window. Ba talks fast, and I only catch a few words: "Mountains...forest...midnight...girl." Đặng Sỹ gets excited at the word "*cô*" – "girl," or "unmarried young woman." (He has two wives.) He sits on my desk almost in Ba's face, and fires rapid questions. Ba answers in a torrent of words and hot breath. I get: "Old man...nephew...house...rally." I have no idea what's going on. Đặng Sỹ turns to me. "We have to go *now*, cố vấn! Very important!"

"*Được*," I say. "Good." *Go where?* I think.

Outside, I pull Đặng Sỹ aside. "Tell me again where we're going?"

Đặng Sỹ looks surprised. "I thought you understood, cố vấn. Hải Lăng District, to meet the old man."

Who's the old man? I think. *What about the girl?*

I drive fast down Highway 1, dodging holes, buses, jeeps, and trucks. Ba sits in back, smoking and picking his yellow, broken teeth. I lean over to Đặng Sỹ and say, "Tell me the story again, slowly."

I slam into a hole. Heat hammers on the hood and roof. Đặng Sỹ slowly, in basic Vietnamese, tells the story, and I catch a few more words: "Guerrilla ... ambush ... capture... tonight."

I still don't get it. Who's the girl? Why do they get so excited about her?

We enter Hải Lăng District Town, dusty markets and tin-roof buildings on the old Mandarin Road to China. We go in Ba's stifling-hot, windowless office. There are no chairs, just a battered desk and a hanging, burned-out light bulb. It looks like no one ever comes here.

Ba cracks the back door, and a sliver of light slices the room, illuminating golden, floating dust. Ba calls sharply into the alley, "You! Old man! Come!"

An old farmer squeezes in and stands looking scared, blinking watery eyes and turning his rice-straw hat in gnarled, trembling hands.

"Tell us the story!" Ba barks. "Talk fast!"

Half-hidden in the gloom, I sweat and struggle to breathe and understand. The old man speaks country dialect in a phlegm-filled, quavering voice. I catch only, "my house... midnight... girl." Again, the girl!

Ba puffs and offers one to Đặng Sỹ. Đặng Sỹ doesn't smoke, but he lights up, too, as he questions the old man. The room fills with hot, stinking haze. The old man turns his conical hat round and round and stammers answers to their questions. They discuss the girl and *đồng* — Vietnamese money — lots of *đồng*. My lungs and head are bursting to get out.

Đặng Sỹ turns to me while Ba finishes with the old man. "Now we go to Major Ngọc, the District Chief, cố vấn. But you talk to him. He won't listen to me; I'm ex-VC and Ba has no standing."

"*Được*," I say. *Talk to him about what?* I think, as Ba pushes the old man into the alley.

We drive to the District Headquarters — gun towers, barbed wire, and sandbags on the edge of town. Fat and greasy Major Ngọc, the District Chief, invites us to his office. We sit in stuffed chairs around a low glass table, while Ngọc's sergeant pours tea into small porcelain cups.

Ngọc ignores Ba and Đặng Sỹ, and speaks to me in French: "Remember the good old days in Huế before Tet '68? Now we're in this outpost of desolation!"

"*Commandant*," I say, "I'm going to ask Đặng Sỹ to tell you why we're here."

"*Non!*" Ngọc explodes, his belly bumping the table and

6

rattling the teacups. *"Pas VC!* Not VC! If not you, Ba, my District Agent, tells me."

Ba leans forward eagerly, sweat shining on the back of his chair. He tells the story I've heard four times. When he says, "girl," Ngọc belly-bumps the table and they talk about *đồng* Ngọc even addresses Đặng Sỹ. They seem to be planning a night operation.

Ngọc leans back grinning, his jowls shaking and shining. *"Bon plan, eh, Monsieur Chiêu Hội?"*

"Très bon plan," I say. *"Très intelligent. Formidable."*

What plan? I think. *And what about the girl?*

Ngọc giggles and calls for more tea. *"Bon,* we go together tonight!" he says. "Big operation! Big success! Big reward!"

I lean away from Ba and Đặng Sỹ and ask in French, "Tell me again about the girl?"

Ngọc laughs. *"Vous n'avez pas compris?* You didn't understand? I thought you were studying Vietnamese! Go ask 'Captain Rose,' my Intelligence Advisor. He'll tell you all about the girl!"

I leave them sipping tea and cross the baking compound to the air-conditioned Advisors' Hut. My friend Captain "Rosie" Rosenberg's not around. He won't return till chow time.

I drive fast through blazing heat back to Quảng Trị City. Đặng Sỹ gets off at his number two wife's house. I drop Ba at the Center.

"Be here at five, cố vấn," Ba breathes in my face. "We need your Scout."

I go to my house and try to sleep. With the ticking of my alarm clock, two words beat in my mind: "Ambush, trap." The whole thing is a set-up. The girl, whoever she is, probably planned it, using herself as bait. And the possibility for leaks and betrayal is *everywhere.* Ba—I don't trust him at all—he'd sell his soul for *đồng.* Major Ngọc could be a VC, except he's absurd. The old farmer *looked* scared, but maybe he's a great actor, maybe he's the mastermind. And Ngọc's sergeant, so interested in our conversation. Đặng Sỹ could *definitely* still be a VC, sharp as he is. They *all* could be VC, all but me. I saw our plan, whatever it was, flowing like a river out to the mountains and forests of Indian Country, and the VC coming to kill us.

I get up, dress in Marine camouflage, and load my M-16. It's almost 5 o'clock. I go out the door and drive to the Center. It's still hot as Hell.

Đặng Sỹ stands frowning in my office. "*Buồn lắm, cố vấn!* Very sad! I can't go with you tonight. I have to stay here on guard. I'm sending the best APT with you—maybe the VC will attack *here* tonight!"

My stomach drops into empty space. Đặng Sỹ's not going. He knows the plan, and he's not going. This *is* a trap! *He's* the one.

"Lúc-Thanh will command the APT," Đặng Sỹ says. "He'll take care of you, cố vấn."

"*Lúc-Thanh.*" I think. "*I'm going on night ambush with Lúc-Thanh.*"

Lúc-Thanh was the most famous of the former VC, a long-time guerrilla with one of their highest medals for "destroying a tank and killing many enemy." Đặng Sỹ's Deputy, he looks like a pirate, with one bad, "rolling" eye from a wound he got fighting U.S. Marines.

Lúc-Thanh looks in and says, "*Mình đi.* We go."

We drive fast down Highway 1, my Scout loaded with ex-VC, and the APT pickup behind, filled with more ex-guerrillas. We bristle like porcupines, with AKs and '16s poking out the windows, and Chinese RPD machine guns on the pickup's cab. Highway 1 is empty—*no one* drives the roads this late. Night, like underground, forests, and mountains, is Indian Country.

"This is the life, eh, cố vấn!" Lúc-Thanh laughs, thrusting his AK into the hot wind. "Go on night operation. Night is the best.

Nhưng đừng bắn cô gái. But don't shoot the girl!"
I look at him and slam into a hole. "I would never shoot a girl!"

We pull up to Ngọc's office in a cloud of dust. He comes out in white T-shirt and plastic slippers. He's not going. He *and* Đặng Sỹ planned this.

"*Quel dommage!*" he says with a long face. "What a pity I can't go! I have to stay here and wait for an important call from my colonel. But I'm sending Lieutenant Tuấn, my Intelligence Officer, and my whole Intelligence Squad, my best men."

Slim, hard-faced Lt. Tuấn steps out of Ngọc's office, then six Intel Squad soldiers, equally tough-looking. Tuấn looks at Lúc-Thanh and snarls, "Those guys are VC! We're not going on operation with them."

Rosie, the Intelligence Advisor, comes out of Ngọc's office, and in dazzlingly fluent Vietnamese says, "Those are *ex*-VC, Lieutenant Tuấn. And I thought you Intel Squad boys weren't afraid of anything."

"Once a VC, *always* a VC," Tuấn growls, not taking his eyes off Lúc-Thanh.

Ngọc pushes forward with his belly rolling. "My Intelligence Squad *is* going—to represent me in the reward!"

Major Stilwell, the Senior District Advisor and grandson of General "Vinegar Joe" Stilwell of World War II fame, comes out of the Advisors' Hut, then black Sgt. Jones, the radio operator and medic, a PRC-25 radio hulking up on his back, and big medic's bag hanging from his shoulder.

While Stilwell and Ngọc talk, I pull Rosie aside. "Tell me the details of what's going on, especially about the girl. I don't like the sound of this. Going after a *girl*?"

Chunky Rosie laughs, his jowls shaking. "Girl can kill you dead as a man. And this is no ordinary girl, this is Annie Oakley!"

9

"Annie Oakley?" Vietnam was full of the American frontier—we had Indian Country, the Oregon Trail, Kit Carson Scouts, Daniel Boone Teams, and more—but Annie Oakley?

Rosie draws me in his office and opens her file. "Her real name is Hoàng Thị Nữ. She's twenty-eight, and a *very* important VC, several high positions, and on the province's 'Most Wanted' list. 'Nữ'—her given name—means 'Woman.' She's unmarried, so the Vietnamese still call her 'cô'—'girl': 'Miss Woman.' We call her 'Annie Oakley' for the two guns she carries, and her magical ways. We've tried to catch her before, my man, but she never shows, gets away, or ambushes *us*. And look at this—several times she's been reported in two places at the same time. She's magic, I tell you. And she's from a long tradition of Vietnamese women warriors."

"*Girl* warrior," I say.

"Yeah—girl warrior. Unmarried woman."

I flip through Annie's file, dozens of agents' reports of her trips down from the mountains and forests, and her night missions in the paddylands. According to the reports, she carries a folding-stock AK-47, and a Soviet officer's K-54 pistol. "How reliable is all this?"

Rosie grins and pats his pocket. "Best intelligence money can buy."

"Have you ever thought this could be a trap?"

"I *always* think that," Rosie says. "I'm from New York, remember?"

We load up. Lt. Tuấn leads with the Intel Squad jammed in Ngọc's jeep. Rosie drives Stilwell's jeep, with Jones and the radio in back. I follow in my Scout, then comes the APT pickup with their Chinese machine guns rattling on the cab. This is already crazy: it's far too late to drive, with the sun dropping behind the "Long Range" Mountains along the Laos border, and a big shadow spreading across the land. Even the hot Lao Wind is dead, the flag of South Vietnam hanging limply on its pole as we rumble out the barbed wire gate and head east into the paddy-sea.

My mind whirls as we fly through the darkening countryside, ditches turning black beside the road. *Annie* — I'm starting to think of her like that — *Annie Oakley. Cô Nữ — Miss Woman.* It's bad to give your enemy a name.

"This is good, eh, cố vấn?" Lúc-Thanh smiles with his eye rolling and pats his AK butt. "Night ambush! But when we meet the girl, *bắt sống!* Capture alive! *Đừng bắn!* Don't shoot, don't kill her!"

"*Không bao giờ,*" I say, squinting into Rosie's dust. "Never. I would *never* kill a girl!"

"*Nguy hiểm ,*" Lúc-Thanh says, staring at me with his good eye. "Very dangerous! When the shooting starts — *nguy hiểm!*"

"I would *never* shoot a girl," I say. "Never."

We cross a rumbling, wooden-plank bridge, turn into the ruins of an old French church, and get out beside a dark, slow-flowing stream. From the bush-grown, broken church walls, a Popular Forces platoon — Ngọc's men — emerges and surrounds us.

"Hey, I know those guys," a sharp-faced PF sergeant says, pointing at Lúc-Thanh. "They're VC. What are they doing out here?"

Rosie fires back in fast Vietnamese, "*Ex*-VC, Sergeant! Anyway, you 'roughpuff' are not going on operation with us. You will stay here and fall asleep on ambush like you *always* do."

The sergeant steps forward with his M-16 in his hand. "Maybe if you get in a fight with the VC tonight, 'Captain Rose,'" he sneers, using a popular Vietnamese girl's name, "those *ex*- VC will fight *you!*"

"At least they fight!" Rosie shoots back, and we follow the APT under the bridge.

More enemies, I think, as we sit and wait beside the dark water. Outside, Ba struts among the PF, probably, I think, telling them our plan. Tuấn and the PF lieutenant stand talking and staring across a fallow paddy at a black treeline. *Even Tuấn could be a VC, I think, and the PF lieutenant, the sergeant, all of them! Maybe we Americans are the only non-VC here!*

Something goes "Plop!" in the stream. Beside me, Lúc-Thanh is agitated, looking at the sky, his eye rolling.

Annie, I think, Miss Nữ — did she lead us out here? Is she waiting, lying like a panther in the gathering night?

Tuấn looks under the bridge and says, *"Minh đi.* We go."

Tuấn forms us in a line beside the stream, Americans in the middle, APT at the end; the PF watch from the bank.

The PF sergeant calls, "Be careful, 'Captain Rose'! Watch your fat ass!"

For once Rosie stays silent. With Tuấn and the Intel Squad leading, we step off at five-meter intervals, and float like ghosts beside the stream.

Lúc-Thanh moves up behind me and whispers, "We have to go faster, cố vấn! The moon will come soon."

We stop and crouch by the stream.

Lúc-Thanh fumes, "The moon!"

Annie's out there, I think, waiting in the paddy. The moon will rise and she'll see us easily, get us all: best of the APT, the Intel Squad, District Advisory Team, including a famous general's grandson, and me. Dead on the Night of Wandering Souls!

Tuấn lies on the stream bank studying the broad paddy to the black treeline.

Why is he waiting? I agonize. To give the moon more chance to rise? Annie will get us for sure!

Tuấn goes over the bank and down into the paddy. We flow behind him like a snake slithering across the giant chessboard of fields, dikes, and elevated paths. At the far end, trees rise like tall black kings and queens. *Here's where it will come*, I think. *Ambush from the dikes, bushes, trees. Here's where Annie will get us!*

Crunching stubble, we race the moon down the river of night. Ahead, near the base of the trees, white sand mounds roll, and a path leads to them. Tuấn weaves among the sandy mounds, and our line snakes behind.

"Hamlet cemetery!" Rosie whispers back. "Watch out for her here!"

Why is Tuấn following this path? I think. I picture Annie and her men lying at the base of the grave-mounds shooting, and our bodies falling, twitching, blood streaking the white sand. I see her hiding like a leopard, her legs drawn up, ready to spring.

Light breaks through the trees, the moon rising huge from the South China Sea and shining on us as we snake among the graves. *Now Annie will get us*, I think. *Now she'll begin firing!*

Our shadows float behind us like our spirits, armed, like us, and on the path among the graves. Tuấn steps out of the cemetery and onto the main hamlet trail, a tunnel through tall, overhanging trees. We join him in our spaced-out line, sweating, breathing hard. On our left are tree-shrouded, thatched houses with small spirit-houses on poles in rice-drying yards, and the smell of incense floating in the air. Right, through arched, leaning, and jumbled bamboo, the stream shines in moonlight.

We walk quietly on the trail. In front of the first house, an old man stands before his spirit-house, rocking, praying, and clutching glowing incense sticks. Suddenly, he hears or senses us, his eyes pop open, and he spins and goes in his house. A quick, soft sound of wood on earth comes out, and I picture him descending into his bunker dug into his packed-earth floor, lowering the trapdoor, and lying in close, damp dark. I feel my heart heavy as my boots hit the trail: how quickly he changed when he saw us, from lost in his prayers to terror. I get a sudden image of combat boots crushing a lotus. We flow on through the trail-tunnel, with soft sounds coming from the stream.

Before the open window of the next house, two women and two girls talk and laugh, their faces illuminated by a candle. Outside in their spirit-house, incense sticks glow like tiny, golden eyes, and smoke wafts off to guide the Wandering Souls of people dead far from home and unable to find their way back. The girls and women don't see us. They keep talking and laughing as if nothing bad is about to happen.

Tuấn kneels ahead at a trail junction, and Ba creeps up to whisper. We crouch in the bamboo and keep watch. Over the shimmering, moonlit stream, a spider-leg bamboo bridge crosses into sinister darkness. Ba points to a house across the junction, where a candle burns in the north window. More soft sounds come from the stream and its brushy banks.

Ba whispers and breathes along our line, "The house with the candle is the old man's— the girl is supposed to come here at midnight."

Tuấn leads us into a shallow, grassy ditch outside the old man's house. Tuấn and Ba whisper under a mango tree, then call Lúc-Thanh and point east, where a trail runs under the moon toward the ocean.

Tuấn comes to the ditch and Rosie translates, "The APT will ambush along the trail to the east. Ba thinks she may come from there, from the dunes along the ocean. The Intel Squad will watch the bridge and old man's house. Advisors stay here in the ditch."

"*What?*" I whisper to Rosie. "They're isolating us here. One grenade, one burst will get us all!"

"Hey, it's a Vietnamese show," Rosie whispers, lying back in the ditch. "We're just Advisors, remember? Relax and enjoy the breeze."

"Like hell," I whisper. I hurry to catch up with the APT, and fall in behind their fast- moving line.

Lúc-Thanh leads us out the back of the hamlet, and up a high dike overlooking broad, fallow fields. We lie in tall, soft grass and moonlight, and look at one of the most beautiful sights I've ever seen: moon-flooded paddy, dikes, paths, distant treeline, and beyond, the rolling, ghostly-white dunes, the long, empty beaches of Quảng Trị, and the sea. I realize again how much I love Vietnam, its magic land, ancient culture, and immersed-in-nature people.

"*Không được!*" Lúc-Thanh whispers, staring into the field. "No good! Lying out there with only a few small bushes. Under this moon? This was *Ba's* idea, and he stays back at the old man's house!"

Lúc-Thanh rises and leads us down the steep bank into the paddy. We walk fast, weaving among strange, dark, curled shapes and piles scattered on the stubble. A disturbing smell rises, and floats with incense from the spirit-houses. Lúc-Thanh quickly places the APT in ambush positions watching the trail, and motions for me to lie beside a small bush.

"Watch along this stretch of trail," he whispers. "Remember, *bắt sống!* Capture alive! *Đừng bắn cô gái!* Don't shoot the girl!"

"I won't!"

I point my rifle at the elevated path and picture Annie and her men walking there. I don't think we can distinguish man from woman on that trail, all wearing baggy black VC clothes and carrying AKs. How will we capture her? What will *they* do when they see us here?

Lúc-Thanh lies on the other side of the bush and points his AK at the trail. The breeze dies, and a terrible stench overwhelms the night. I twist back, looking for the source. Ominous, dark, curled shapes and piles lie close to my legs and boots. I flash on the high dike across the back of the hamlet, the scattered bushes, and the dark shapes on the stubble. Of course! This is the hamlet toilet! And we're locked into ambush positions here!

"It stinks here, cố vấn," Lúc-Thanh whispers through the bush. "It stinks real bad!"

"No shit, Lúc-Thanh!" I want to say, but I don't know how.

"*Ba*," Lúc-Thanh mutters through gritted teeth. "Ba sent us out here!"

We lie rigid, afraid to move, shallow-breathing, and staring at the trail. No VC come to relieve us. Seconds, minutes, hours of foul stench pass, and *wishing* the VC would come. *There's no shit-smell like human shit-smell*, I think. *Ba sent us out here!*

I look at the trail. I can't imagine Annie appearing here. She wouldn't come to such a place.

Before midnight, a dark shadow floats from the hamlet, creeps among us whispering, and finds Lúc-Thanh. "Lieutenant Tuấn wants everybody back at the old man's house. *Trời ơi*, good heavens, it stinks here!"

We walk carefully, as if crossing a minefield. I'm hardly thinking of Annie and the VC. I just want to breathe out the stink and move freely, without fear, again. Back at the ditch, Rosie, Stilwell, and Jones look pretty casual lying in soft grass with fresh breezes blowing.

"Where've you *been*?" Rosie whispers. "You guys stink!"

The old man's house is dark; the whole hamlet is in heavy, sinister silence. At the trail-junction, Tuấn and Ba sit flanking a young, wild-haired VC. Behind the VC, his AK lies radiating dark power — it's just come from "out there," the mountains and forests of Indian Country.

"Annie's bodyguard," Rosie whispers. "He's the old man's

nephew. He wants to rally, but for us to make it look like he's being captured. He's scared to death of her."

I go over and sit behind the VC and beside the AK, looking down at it in awe, and listening to Tuấn and Ba's questions.

"Where is she now?" Ba breathes into the VC's face. "You *must* know!"

The VC turns around and looks fearfully at me. "No, I don't! She doesn't tell us anything—only where to meet her, not even always when."

"Who are her contacts here?" Tuấn demands. "Where do they live?"

The VC looks wildly up and down the trail. "I don't know, she doesn't tell us. Please, get me away from here! She's coming soon!"

Tuấn and Ba get up and leave the VC sitting with me. I take his AK over to the ditch. Tuấn calls Lúc-Thanh and they whisper and gesture toward the spidery, bamboo-pole bridge.

Tuấn comes and Rosie translates: "They think she's coming soon. Intel Squad will watch the bridge and this side of the house, APT the trail and the other side. Advisors stay here in the ditch."

"No way," I whisper. I hurry after the APT, and catch up in the trail-tunnel.

In front of the old man's house, Lúc-Thanh places the young ex-guerilla Bốn and me. "You two watch the trail and the door," he whispers. He looks at me, his eye rolling. "*Bắt sống!* Capture alive! Don't shoot her!"

"*Không bao giờ!*" I whisper. "Never!"

Lúc-Thanh vanishes down the trail, and Bốn motions for us to back slowly into the bamboo lining the stream. We lie down with young bamboo rising all around us, and our rifles low and aimed at the old man's house. I point my muzzle at the door, deep in shadow under shaggy thatch. I try to imagine the door sliding open and someone coming out. Could I tell Annie from a man there?

Bốn sees me aiming and shoves my muzzle to the ground. "*Đừng bắn cô gái!*" he whispers. "Don't shoot the girl!"

"I *won't!*" I whisper. Damn, why do they all think I'm going to *shoot* her?

Overhead, the bamboo creaks, sighs, and falls silent. Something goes "Plop!" in the stream. Across the trail, the old man's house looms black and deathly still. Suddenly, something happens. A wave of energy, unseen and powerful, surges through the bamboo, hits Bốn and me, and passes on. Bốn and I raise up on our elbows and look at each other big-eyed, slack-jawed. An electric, invisible force has just swept through the bamboo and us.

"It's the girl!" Bốn whispers. "She's coming!"

We squirm low into leaves and dirt, hearts hammering, rifles trembling. Queen Adrenaline starts to rule the night. A black phantom-shape—not solid, it seems, but vibrating waves of energy—silently floats across the old man's rice-drying yard and enters the house.

"*Đừng bắn cô ta!*" Bốn gasps. "Don't shoot her!"

Two *more* phantoms cross the rice-drying yard and disappear inside the house. *Three* people in there with the old man and his wife. But who?

Lúc-Thanh's shout from the house shatters the night. "Miss Nữ! Come out and rally! You don't have to be a prisoner!"

The night tumbles back into silence, now vibrating, burning fiercely. I picture all around the house men lying electrified and ready to shoot.

Lúc-Thanh shouts again. "Miss Nữ! We know you're down there! The house is surrounded! Come out and rally! You don't have to be a prisoner!"

The night starts to fall back into silence, then the house explodes. Grenade! Everything begins happening at once, or at such hyper-speed that time melts into itself, and consciousness starts to lose its grip. Crashing, grunts, shouts, a table overturning, someone running through a wall! Shots! *Bam! Bam!*

Wild thrashing sounds erupt in the banana patch at the corner of the house! Bốn and I jump up and stand on the trail staring into moonlight and shadows. A black phantom flashes across the trail, and smashes like a wild deer into the bamboo bordering the stream. More crashing and smashing, the deer-phantom fighting its way toward the water.

I feel something inside me happen, something shifts, and I only later understand what it is. *I've just fallen in love with my enemy, with her energy, power, courage, and wildness.*

"The girl!" Bốn says. "She's running away!"

Bốn runs up the path and I follow, boots and heart pounding. All around the night comes alive with shouts and running shadows. I have no idea who's us or them. More shots! *Bababam!*

"*Đừng bắn!*" Lúc-Thanh shouts. "*Bắt sống!*"

Bốn pushes into the bamboo where Annie flashed across the path and I follow, plowing ahead, whip-lashed. Sudden silence ahead — she's stopped! Now *she* ambushes *us*!

Splash!

"She jumped!" Bốn says. "She's in the water!" He pushes forward and I follow, gouged, panting, sweating.

We force our way to the bank and stare stunned. Annie's already at midstream, *throwing* herself toward the opposite side, moonlit water streaming from her black pants, shirt, and hair. She's getting away!

Bababam! Bốn begins shooting into the water ahead of her. *Bababam! Bababam!* Deadly bullet-fountains spring up in her path, and she *throws* herself toward them. She looks like a sea lion lunging through the water, fighting for the darkness of the other side.

Bababam! APT and Intel Squad fight their way to the bank and fire, shooting up more bullet-fountains in her path. She throws herself *eagerly* toward them. *Bababam!*

"*Đừng bắn!*" Lúc-Thanh shouts from the shaking bridge. *Bắt sống! Cô Nữ!* Stop! You don't have to be a prisoner!"

All around, the night writhes like a great glowing snake. Blood pounds, guns explode, flames burst from barrels. I begin to shoot with everybody else, ahead of her, trying to make her stop, turn, anything, just don't get away. *Bababababam!* She streams moonlight and water as she throws herself toward the bullet-fountains. It's the first time I've fired at a visible person, and she's a *girl*, she's Annie Oakley! *Bababam!* My M-16 jams, and I drop to one knee, fumble, clear it, rise, and shoot again: *Bababababam!* Fountains spout all across Annie's path, and she lunges forward as if she wants to *bathe* in them.

She's getting away! I think. No, stop, you can't get away!

Bababababam!

"*Cô Nữ!*" Lúc-Thanh shouts down from the bridge. "Stop! Rally! Join us!"

Bababababam!

"*Đừng bắn! Bắt sống!*"

Another terrible image flashes across the reality of Annie's flight: I'm a kid at the Iowa State Fair, shooting-gallery ducks crossing a metal pond, and I'm knocking them down with a real .22 rifle. *Bababababam!*

Tuấn runs onto the bridge and shoots up a parachute flare. It arcs over the stream and comes down hissing, burning, and making giant shadows sway and dance. The hamlet is bathed in yellow chemical light. Trees, houses, the bridge all sway and dance. Everything seems beyond human scale. Annie streams flare-lit, moonlit water as she hurls herself toward the bullet-fountains. *Bababam! Bababam!* It's obvious she'd rather *die* than be captured or join us. Bốn runs for the bridge. Everyone's running and shouting. I'm the only one left here to stop her.

Bababam!

"*Đừng bắn! Bắt sống!*"

Annie suddenly changes course and begins to lunge downstream. I see her face in desperate profile, *and* where she's heading, a dry ditch across the stream from me that comes in from the darkness like an arrow. If she can get there, she can run up it and escape! Only I see this, only I can stop her. "Oh, God," I hear myself say, "I'm going to have to kill her."

Rocked by shooting and lit by adrenaline, my mind shouts more dark words: "We're going to fail. We *can't* fail. Oh, God, I'm going to have to kill her!"

"*Đừng bắn! Bắt sống!*"

Bababam!

I see her eye, like a wild animal trying to escape; I point the muzzle at her head. "Oh, God, I'm going to kill her!"

Bababam!

I shoot a burst and see bullet-fountains fly up on both sides of her head. She struggles out of the water and falls to one knee on the muddy bank just short of the ditch. "Oh God, I hit her!"

She staggers up and begins sprinting down the ditch, soles of her bare feet flying. She's getting away! We can't fail, we can't *lose*! I aim at her back and pull the trigger. "Oh God, I'm going to kill her!"

Babababam!

Dirt-fountains shoot up on both sides of her feet. She pitches forward and is swallowed by the ditch banks and shadows.

Oh God, I've killed her! screams in my mind. *I killed Annie, I killed Miss Nữ! I shot her in the back!* I turn to the dark bridge and start to sink. I grip my rifle. I don't know if I can live with this.

Shouts explode across the stream! Shots! *BOOM!* Grenade! Another!

I run to the quaking bridge and cross fast. I don't know what's happening, but I want to throw myself into it. *If I could bring her back I would.* I dash wildly across a stubble field to ghostlike figures gathering around a still form on the ground. I push through staring APT and look down in horror at Annie, crumpled on the moonlit stubble, her head covered in blood. I feel I want to die; I want the earth to swallow me. *I killed her!* I think. *I shot her in the head!*

Lúc-Thanh pushes in with his bad eye rolling. "Why did you shoot, cố vấn?" he demands. "You didn't hear me shout, '*Đừng bắn!*'?"

"*Xin lỗi,*" I say. "I'm sorry." It sounds pitiful and weak. I look down at her, blood shining in the moonlight. "I'm so sorry she's dead."

"*Không chết!*" Lúc-Thanh laughs. "*Bị thương!* Not dead! Wounded! Lucky for you!"

"*Bị thương?*" I say, feeling a sudden reprieve, and whirling to look at her bloody head. "But how bad?"

Lúc-Thanh grins and pulls his ear. "Only her ear! Ear bleeds a lot, and not you! APT got her with grenades, knocked her out. And a piece of shrapnel cut her ear! Lucky for *them* they didn't kill her!"

Sgt. Jones parts the forming circle and kneels behind Annie's head. He gently pulls back her wet hair, peers at her ear closely, and wraps her head round and round with a long, olive-green bandage.

"Earlobe bleeds a lot," he says, looking up at Stilwell and Rosie. "I don't see any other wounds. *Maybe* she's unconscious — I'd say it's fifty-fifty."

RICHARD L. STEVENS

"We have to go *now*, cố vấn!" Lúc-Thanh says, pulling my sleeve. "We're making too much noise! The VC will try to get her back!"

Rosie squats and carefully picks Annie up, cradling her in his thick arms. I think I see her stiffen, then go limp into real or feigned unconsciousness again, her hair and head hanging, bare feet dangling, bouncing. We walk back toward the bridge like a holy procession. I follow a little to the side of Rosie, where I can see her head, her face almost completely hidden by the long bandage. Rosie walks solemnly, like a knight bearing a queen. What is it like to hold that wet, dark power?

I quick-step to the bridge, stand aside, and watch as Rosie approaches with Annie. He walks like he's in a trance. He steps onto the trembling bamboo, sways, rights himself, uses her body as a balance, and flows across to the other side. We all cross, shaking the bridge.

I inch along, looking down at black water with the full moon floating. Where the flare burned and Annie lunged, muddy ripples spread from our crossing. I hear my rifle exploding and see my bullets fountain again, and the way she *threw* herself toward them. The way she ran, jumped, swam, the courage she has—who *is* she? Where does she get the physical skills, the motivation, the power? And what happens to her now?

Rosie carries her into a thatched, open-sided, water-buffalo shed just off the trail, and lays her down on a pile of straw. APT and Intel Squad crowd in, everybody buzzing with electricity and staring at Annie. The buffalo pulls back in a dark corner, his eyes terror-struck, nose running, horns trembling. Annie lies curled on the straw in a fetal position, and for a moment I think of Mary in the manger. Everyone's talking at once, telling what they did.

Lúc-Thanh pushes in and pulls my sleeve. "We have to keep

23

moving, cố vấn! We're making too much noise! No one's even keeping guard!"

Tuấn whispers with two of his men and they disappear into the black trail-tunnel. Ba crowds in and looks down at Annie. Rosie stands by Annie's feet; I stand by her head protecting her. The two Intel men return with two scared-looking peasant women carrying a long bamboo pole. Tuấn spits words at the women, and they put the bamboo down.

"Annie's aunts, I think," Rosie whispers. "They raised her. They live near the old man."

She's listening, I think, looking at Annie. *She knows everything.*

Tuấn snarls at the aunts and jerks his head at Annie. The women rise and come in the shed, passing through us as if we were invisible. They grasp Annie's shoulders and feet, and half-carry, half-drag her out and lay her by the pole. Tuấn tosses them rope, and they tie Annie's wrists and ankles to the big bamboo. As they crouch and work near her feet and head, I see something passing between Annie and them! No sounds, nothing visible, but *something*.

Tuấn sees it too. "*Mau đi!*" he snaps. "Hurry up!"

The aunts squat at the ends of the pole, struggle it onto their shoulders, and stand, weaving under Annie's weight.

"*Đi!!*" Tuấn orders, and the women stagger off bent-legged, Annie's body hanging, rocking.

What must the pain be like? I think, *Her ankles, wrists? How can she keep feigning unconsciousness?*

We circle out the back of the hamlet, on a roundabout route toward the church ruins. I walk just to the side and a little behind Annie, unable to tear my eyes off her, wanting to be close to her radiating energy. Her hair hangs, her body rocks. The aunts stumble and strain across the broad field. We look like we're on safari. Annie's our captured lioness, swaying beneath the pole.

24

Now comes the ambush, I think. *All the noise we made, the parachute flares! Annie's men will rise up from underground, race after us as the moon goes down, and catch up to the aunts' painfully – or willfully – slow gait. Annie! What is it like for her hanging, swinging from the pole? Where does she get the courage, the power?*

Lúc-Thanh walks up beside me. Together we watch her hair almost brush the earth. I want to ask him where she gets the strength and dedication, but I don't know those words.

I try, "You know how she ran, swam, didn't care if we killed her, but wasn't going to stop?"

Lúc-Thanh turns toward me, his war-ravaged face dark and his bad eye rolling. *"Không có cô gái như vậy ở trong này,"* he says sadly. "There are no girls like that on this side."

I wonder in a flash if he's sad because there are no girls like that on this side, or because he's *on* this side, or what side *is* he on? Then I think of all the Vietnamese girls and women I've met in almost three years here. I know amazingly beautiful, strong, brave women, but not one who could have done what Annie did tonight, or probably even what she's enduring now. I don't know *anyone*, man or woman, of *any* nationality, who could have done what she did. And I almost killed her. *Oh, God, please forgive me, and what will I have to pay for this?*

The moon sinks behind the western mountains as we approach the dark church ruins. Wandering souls crossing the field, we bear our wild being into captivity.

2

INSIDE THE WIRE

> ... the war has separated hundreds of families, children
> from their fathers, and wives from their husbands. At
> the same time, thousands of people sacrifice their lives
> for their country's independence and freedom. I am a
> Vietnamese woman, born and raised in that spirit.
>
> —Hoàng Thị Nữ

We pass through the wire and enter the ruins. The church looms over us like a relic from the Middle Ages. Dark shapes — the PF — emerge from hiding places among the bushes and broken walls. Tuấn snarls an order and the aunts lower Annie to the ground and squat, cowering at her head and feet. Annie lies still, looking like part of the earth.

Tuấn growls at the aunts again, and working fearfully, they untie Annie, shoulder the pole, go out through the wire, and are swallowed in black. I look across the paddy at the dark tree line, where the cemetery meets the hamlet. What news is passing fast there now from the aunts to her people?

"They've captured her! She's at the church! We have to get her back!"

The hard-faced PF sergeant pushes through and stares down at Annie. "What, Captain Rose?" he says to Rosie in Vietnamese. "You caught a big female fish?"

Rosie ignores him, talks low to Tuấn and Ba, and translates.

"They want to take her back to District HQ. They say it's too dangerous to stay here."

"Drive the roads at night?" I say. "That's crazy!"

Tuấn steps between us. "We're going. Cố vấn, we'll put her in your Scout."

Tuấn's men are already on the move. Two bend to grasp her shoulders, a third a leg. I grab her other leg and we carry her wet body to the Scout, her hair almost brushing the ground. Her calf muscle is warm through her black pants and hard as a rock. I feel my heart racing as I drop the tailgate and we slide her in. Too far! Her head bumps the back of the front seat and her chin wedges against her chest. I stare at her and can't move. *I can't leave her like that.*

All around, Vietnamese are climbing aboard, engines are starting, and the night is vibrating in black. Lúc-Thanh gets into the front seat and urges me to hurry.

I take a breath and crawl in back, into the small space filled with her. She radiates stream water, dark earth, wildness, and energy. I gently grasp her shoulders and try to pull her down. The moment my hands touch her, a deep, terrible sound bursts from within, a moan, but also containing, "Don't touch me!"

Clumsily, I back out, stumble around the Scout, climb into the driver's seat, and grip the steering wheel. My hands are still wet from her. Her being fills my mind, and my heart is breaking for her. *What will happen to her now?* Tuấn drives out of the churchyard and onto the road, and Rosie and I follow, lights off, rumbling across the wooden bridge. *Ambush!* I think, as I picture the dark journey ahead. *Ambush, mines, they'll get us for sure!*

Behind us, the ruins recede. Ahead, mountains roll across a star-studded sky. Tuấn drives fast and we follow in his dust cloud, racing between black irrigation ditches, and past small temples, squat, dark houses like thatched mushrooms, and the vast paddy-sea, Annie's country. Behind me, she lies rocking and vibrating on the metal floor. *What can she be thinking? Or is she just waiting for her chance to strike back?*

Lúc-Thanh pokes his AK out the window and rolls his bad eye at me. "Good eh, cố vấn? Capture, don't kill."

"Yes, good," I mutter, staring into roiling dust and darkness. Inside my head, other words beat like drums: *What will happen to her now?*

Behind me, Annie lies silently between the boots of six APT, arm over her face, body rocking with the Scout. I want to know everything about her. Where does she get the courage to do what she does? Where does she get the physical skills, the strength? What is her motivation?

Ahead, Tuấn pushes speed to the limit of mad-dash driving, trying to pass through Annie's countryside before her men can react. *Any VC could get us out here, even a lone guerrilla seeing opportunity coming in our roaring dust-plume flight.*

Suddenly the District Compound looms out of the dust and darkness like a lonely outpost in Indian Country, towers, walls, and guns against the sky. We stop at the gate, still flying inside, and wait while the guard drags open the barbed-wire barricade.

What will happen to her now? I think as I drive through the wire and Major Ngọc's soldiers pour out of their bunkers and barracks. Ngọc comes out among them in his underwear, belly fat jiggling over his shorts.

"Sergeant!" he shouts to the aide trailing behind him. "Bring refreshments! The heroes are back with their big catch. Where is she? Let's see her!"

Skinny teenage soldiers surround my Scout, open the tailgate, and drag her out. Led by a dark, sharp-faced lieutenant, they carry her lifted high above the crowd into a small sandbagged building.

I jump out and confront Ngọc. "Where are they going with her?"

He throws his head back and laughs. "Infirmary!" he says. "She's wounded, isn't she? She needs treatment. The reward is for her *vivante*! Alive! Here, my sergeant has Cokes and oranges for you. Heroes! You got her!"

I grab a Coke and two oranges and force my way into the crowd packing the small infirmary. It feels like when she was in the buffalo shed, everyone talking at once, and the space crackling with energy like an electrical storm. Unable to push closer to her by tight-packed bodies, I look over tousled heads and see a heart-tearing sight, Annie lying naked on a wooden table under the glare of a bare bulb. She's conscious now and writhing, turning her face into the table and trying to cover herself with her hands. Under that terrible light and with jostling, jeering young soldiers all around, she looks pale, petite, and frail. *Where, then, does she get the power to do what she does?*

Big and black Sergeant Jones, using his medic's bag like a shield, bulls his way through the crowd, tossing Vietnamese out of his way like dolls. Standing behind Annie, he gently unwraps the bloody bandage from her head and drops it on the floor. Reaching into his big black bag, he pulls out shiny steel surgical scissors, raises them high under the bare bulb, and with two quick snips cuts a V-shaped chunk out of Annie's left ear.

I stand paralyzed as blood spurts like a fountain from her ear and Jones cleans the wound and winds another long bandage around her head.

"That's my job done here," he says over the crowd to Rosie. "She doesn't have any other visible wounds."

"I'll take over now," the sharp-faced lieutenant says in Vietnamese. "Everybody out!"

"My counterpart, Lieutenant Giang," Rosie says, as we meet

outside the door. "He'll conduct the interrogations."

"Oh." I feel something drop inside me. "What will that be like?"

"Usually, he doesn't let me see. He uses what he calls his 'punctuation stick.' When he thinks his subjects are lying, he 'punctuates' them."

"Big Victory!" Ngọc says, joining us with a bag in his hand. "We'll get plenty of intelligence from her. Maybe boost the reward! More Cokes, oranges?"

We decline and Ngọc goes off with his bag and his sergeant trailing.

"You can sleep in the advisors' hooch," Rosie says. "Tuấn's getting your APT settled."

I walk away from the infirmary with a heavy heart. Inside the dark advisors' hut, Rosie points to an empty top bunk. At the far end, Sergeant Jones hangs his bag on a nail and heads for the shower. An air conditioner hums in the wall.

I climb into the bunk, lie on my side on a scratchy Army blanket, and look out a small, barred window. *What can be happening to her now?* I turn on my back, look up at the ceiling, and clasp my hands across my chest. I feel like a corpse. *When I die, I'll look like this. What have we done here, and what can be happening to her now?*

I turn my head and look through the barred window again, at the mountains dark in the west. *That's where she comes from, out there in the wild forests of the Ho Chi Minh Trail. I wish she was still there, and free.*

Someone snores. Sergeant Jones pads back from the shower and crawls into his bunk. I look at the ceiling. No way I can fall asleep with all these thoughts of her. *What does she look like? I still haven't seen her face clearly. What is she like? I want to know all about her, I want what she has, the power.*

30

I fall asleep and into a vivid dream of her. We sit in a quiet place, heads close and talking. Her hair falls to her shoulders. I see her face for the first time. She looks like the beautiful and famous "Miss Moon" of Huế, English teacher at Đồng Khánh Girls' School, first woman in Huế to dare to wear a mini-skirt in public. Like Miss Moon, Annie in my dream studied English in London and has the same soft, rhythmic, British-Vietnamese accent. We lean closer, talk low. Her hair brushes my arm. We fall in love. I start to ask her the secret of her courage and strength.

I wake up. My head is filled with the dream and her. I saw her face! She looks like Miss Moon! I try to return to the dream but can't. I look through the bars. There's a hint of light in the sky. Got to get moving.

Dropping softly to the floor amid the snores of Rosie and the others, I pull on my pants, lace up my boots, and go looking for Lúc-Thanh. On the lanai floor outside Ngọc's office he and the APT sleep scattered as if rolled there out of a giant's dice cup. I shake Lúc-Thanh's shoulder and say, "Wake up. We'll go back."

His bad eye squints from under his hat. "No good," he says. "Too early. Maybe mines on the road."

"No, I heard the first bus," I say. "We can make it."

Grumbling, he rousts the APT up and we walk to the Scout carrying our rifles. Ahead, a guard stands outside the compound's dungeon, a French-built concrete cube, thick-walled, no windows, and a barred steel door.

"She's in there," Lúc-Thanh says, his eye rolling. "It's a bad place. Why are you in such a hurry?"

I blaze back to Quảng Trị dodging early-morning buses and trucks, drop the APT off at the Center, and drive fast on the dusty street past the Citadel moat and walls toward my house. I can't get her off my mind. I have to go back and see her. I have to find out everything about her.

31

I wait impatiently while the old Vietnamese guard drags open my iron and barbed-wire gate. He salutes and I drive through and park in the tight space between the compound wall and the agriculture advisor's house. I walk quickly to my room in the old servants' quarters out back, stripping off my camouflage shirt and pants and leaving them in the adjoining laundry room for my maid, Mrs. Nga.

I shower, shave, rub on Mennen's Speedstick, dress in civvies, grab my pistol, and go back out to my Scout. With the pistol on the seat beside me, I drive to the PX in the barbed-wire-surrounded U.S. MACV Advisors' Compound, buy a box of chocolates and a carton of Salem cigarettes, and put them in a bag with the two oranges I got from Ngọc. Then I point the Scout for Vinh's house at the edge of Quảng Trị City, where the last houses meet the paddies, tombs, and temples. Vinh is my interpreter, and I need him badly now. My Vietnamese is not good enough for what I want to say and hear from her.

I stop in front of his family's small house, young rice growing right up to the door. On the porch, tall and handsome Vinh stands with his girlfriend, Cô Lan, "Miss Orchid," one of the beauties of Quảng Trị. He does not look happy to see me.

He comes out to the Scout, looking nervously up and down the street for the jeeps of the Draft Patrol. He's dodging the draft working for us Americans and as a sometimes student at Huế University.

"I'm off, you know," he laughs. "You said three days for the Wandering Souls Holiday, remember?"

"Get in," I say. "I just want to talk to you a minute."

He gets in, moving the pistol and the bag over, and sinking low in the seat. "Mind if I smoke? Lan doesn't like me to smoke around her."

He pulls a Marlboro from behind his ear, lights up with

a flip-top Zippo and blows out the window. Vinh looks like a young Vietnamese Elvis Presley, styling his hair and growing his sideburns like Elvis. Lan, in violet *áo dài* and white silk pants blowing in the summer wind, waves at me and wags her finger at Vinh. He sinks lower and blows another big puff out the window.

"So what do you want to talk to me about? Did you catch the VC girl?"

A chill goes through me. "How do you know about that?"

"Đặng Sỹ told me. He said you and Lúc-Thanh were going after an important VC girl. Did you catch her?"

"Vinh, I need you to come to Hải Lăng with me just for a couple of hours."

He sits up. "No way, I'm on holiday, remember? Lan's off, too. Oh, and she's having a party. She wants you to come. I'll tell you when."

"Yes, good, but I need you now. It's very important. I'll give you two more days off, three."

Vinh puffs again and squints at me. "Go to Hải Lăng to do what?"

"Just talk. Short conversation."

"With who?"

"Her, the VC girl."

"No way!" Vinh says, reaching for the door. "I don't want to talk to her. I got nothing to say to her."

I put my hand on his arm. "No, it's OK, Vinh, we've talked to lots of ralliers."

"Ralliers! She's no rallier. She's a real VC. I don't even want to see her."

"Just a few minutes," I beg. "A few questions, not even any military stuff. I'll give you four days off, a week. A week of total freedom with Lan."

Lan walks back and forth on the porch, her body willowy and her *áo dài* blowing.

"Down and back. No other places, no other people. Just her," Vinh says. "I have to tell Lan."

"Not where we're going or who we're talking to."

"I would never tell her that. I don't even want to know myself."

He gets out, throws down his cigarette, and joins Lan on the porch. They talk, his back to me. She smiles at me over his shoulder, maybe at the "seven days." In my rear-view mirror as we drive away, I see her get on her bicycle and ride off down the street, her *áo dài* streaming behind her.

Is she setting a message in motion? I wonder. *They're leaving Quảng Trị now and going to visit her!* No, it's hard to imagine Vinh and Lan as VC—but maybe that's the best reason for imagining they *are*.

"Maybe she won't talk to us," Vinh mutters, and he taps out another Marlboro.

I drive fast, dodging buses, trucks, bikes, scooters, Jeeps. Everyone plays chicken on Highway 1, competing for the mostly unbroken middle of the road, where there's less chance the VC have planted mines. We hurtle toward each other and swerve fast at the last possible moment, slam and bounce on the potholed, broken side, and veer back to center. Made it!

Sand dunes, dry fields, scattered thatched houses, hard sun, blue sky. Vinh mostly stays silent. I think constantly of Annie. I turn off the highway at the Hải Lăng market and stop at the gate of the District Compound.

"Maybe they won't let us see her," Vinh says glumly, as the guard drags open the barbed-wire gate.

I park and we walk through the heat and dust to Rosie's office. Vinh withdraws to light up in the shade of the Advisors'

Hut. "This is a bad idea," he calls as I go in Rosie's door.

Rosie looks up from a pile of files. "Well, well, what have we here? Camouflage man morphs into . . . what? Boy, you smell different, too! What's in the bag?"

I shift on my feet. "How is she?"

"Who?"

"You know who: Annie Oakley, the VC girl."

Rosie's broad face darkens and his big jowls droop. "She's as well as can be expected."

"Meaning?"

"She's not talking. Usually they talk by now. She's hard-core. She claims she's just a messenger, and she doesn't know what the message was. She just delivers it to a hollow tree. She says over and over, 'I'm no one, just a woman.' Giang's been using his punctuation stick a lot. Mostly he keeps me away."

I feel dizzy, sick at the thought of Giang's stick flashing, exploding all over her frail, wounded body. "I want to see her."

Rosie tilts his head toward the adjoining office. "I'll have to ask Giang. He's not in a good mood."

"Ask him."

Rosie goes out and comes back. "He says she won't talk to you. But you get a short visit. If you learn anything valuable, tell him."

Heart pumping, I turn to leave. He steps between me and the door.

"What's in the bag?" he says, and he looks into it. "Trying to convert her to capitalism?"

I walk in a daze to the dungeon, Rosie and Vinh a half-step behind. Rosie talks fast Vietnamese to the guard. The guard replies in heavy country dialect and Rosie translates. "He won't go in with you. He says it stinks in there."

"I don't want him in there," I say.

"Yes, we do," Vinh says. "I don't want to be alone with her."

"You'll be all right," Rosie says. "She's unconscious most of the time or faking it. I'm not going in. Giang brings her out for interrogation."

The guard says something and Rosie translates, "He'll have to lock you in. Knock hard three times when you want to come out."

"Locked inside with her?" Vinh says, staring at the door. "This is not a good idea."

The guard approaches the door grinning, M-16 slung over his shoulder. "Beat, beat, beat!" he says to Vinh. "You have to beat hard so I'll hear you."

"We don't have to do this," Vinh says to me. "It won't be good in there."

The guard pulls and tugs the heavy iron bar till it begins to rumble and squeak across the door. My heart speeds up. She's in there.

"Light switch on the left," the guard says to Vinh. "Turn it off when you come out."

Vinh nods weakly and looks like he's going to be sick. The bar rumbles and clinks to a stop. Holding the double door shut, the guard says, "I'm only opening it a little. The stink is evil in there."

Turning aside and covering his mouth and nose, the guard cracks the door and pushes us into hot darkness thick with an unbelievably rotten stench of human urine, feces, and misery. Immediately the door slams behind us and the big iron bar begins to rumble and squeak.

"The light, Vinh!" I say, daring to open my mouth in Hell, beginning to sweat, and feeling coated with stench. "He said on the left."

"I can't find it!" Vinh says in terror.

The blackness is as thick and total as the smell, but there's a wild, powerful presence looming somewhere in the dark. Vinh fumbles in near panic along the hard, pitted wall. I find the switch and flick it on.

Now we see, as well as smell, Hell. This is a room where people are tortured and murdered. Annie lies under a bare bulb on her side on a battered wooden table, knees drawn up in a fetal position, dirty bare soles toward us, head bandaged, face turned to the brown-stained, pock-marked wall. In the far corner stands a bucket caked with black and brown ancient and fresh excrement. Vinh and I shallow-breathe, sweat, and stare. The heat and stench have us paralyzed. The air, what air is there, feels dead, rotten, dying.

Annie doesn't move, doesn't acknowledge our existence. She—and we—could be part of the terrible walls. Vinh looks at me, jerks his head at the door, his eyes wild and pleading, "Let's get out of here!"

Vinh and I are slammed helplessly against the door, while she lies there radiating immense energy and silently enduring the hellish conditions. I prod Vinh to say something but his jaws are clamped shut. He shakes his head.

I have to say something. Finally, I choke out a question: "*Vào được không*? Can we come in?" Hearing my cracked voice and that idiotic question, I feel even more helpless and under her spell.

She doesn't move. Finally, her voice comes from the wall. "I'm your prisoner. You can do anything you want with me."

I elbow Vinh and say, "Ask her if we can just talk to her. Tell her we're not interested in military information. We just want to know about her."

In a quavering voice, Vinh asks, and her voice again comes from the wall. "I'm no one, just a messenger, just a woman."

In the space while I try to think what to say next, she utters a low moan and says, "*Đau nặng*, it hurts too much. I can't talk anymore."

My words tumble out. "Vinh, tell her I was there last night. I saw her run and swim through our bullets. I want to know how she can do that, where she gets the courage and motivation."

Vinh chokes out a stream of words.

"You were trying to kill me," she says without moving. "Anyone would do the same. I'm no one. Just a woman."

She's talking! I think wildly. *She's talking to us.*

She begins to move. She rises up on her elbow, twists her head back, sweeps her gaze past me as if I wasn't there, and pins Vinh to the door with her look. Her face is swollen, brutal, hard. She does *not* look like Miss Moon of Huế. She stares at Vinh and turns back to the wall.

"Out!" Vinh says, and he turns to bang on the door. "I'm afraid of her. She's not going to talk anymore."

I grab his arm and say, "Ask her what she wants for Vietnam."

Sweat pouring, Vinh stammers, "The American asks what you want for Vietnam."

For a moment she's silent. Then her voice comes from the wall, "*Hoà bình*. Peace."

"*Hoà bình!*" I say excitedly. "I also want peace. We can work together."

"No," she says. "Americans get out of Vietnam and let Vietnamese solve their own problems."

"What problems?" I ask through Vinh.

"Rich people own all the land. Poor people have nothing."

She's talking to us! "Vinh, ask her why she joined the VC."

Vinh asks and she stirs, rises on her elbow, twists back, sweeps past me, and again pins Vinh to the door with her look. "*You* know," she says, and she turns back to the wall.

Vinh panics and looks at me wild-eyed and trembling. "I don't know why she said that!" he stammers. "I don't know her. I don't know why she's a VC!"

"It's OK," I say. "Don't worry about it."

He twists and raises his fist to beat on the door.

"Wait. I still have these—" I raise the bag.

"She won't take those. Out!"

"Try! Ask her, tell her I want to leave these." I dare to step forward and put the bag on the scarred table beside her back.

In a low voice, Vinh says, "The American wants to give you oranges, chocolate, and tobacco."

Again, she's silent. Hot, rotten air flows in and out of our lungs. Our hearts beat and our blood pumps. Finally, she says, "I can't accept those things. Take them away."

Vinh hammers wildly on the door. "*Đi ra ngoài!*" he shouts. "Go outside! Open!"

We hear the bar squeak and begin to rumble. Vinh presses against the door as if he wants to walk through it.

I take the bag and look one last time at Annie's bare feet, black pants, slim back, tousled hair, and stained bandage around her head.

The bar clunks to a stop and the guard shouts, "Turn off the light! I'm opening only a little. Come out fast."

The door cracks open and Vinh bolts, squeezing through and forgetting the light. Heart splitting, I look once more at her, turn off the light, and step outside. Behind me, the guard slams the door, and the bar begins its rumbling journey.

Vinh's already halfway to the Scout and pulling out his Marlboros. I scuff through the dust toward Rosie's office feeling dizzy, filthy, and heavy as lead. Rosie comes out and we stand under a roof overhang in hot wind.

"Damn!" Rosie says, moving upwind. "Why is it you always

stink so bad?" He looks at the bag. "So, you didn't convert her to capitalism. Did she say anything?"

"Not much. That she's just a messenger, just a woman." I hand him the bag. "Can you try to get those to her?"

Rosie snorts. "Through the guard? Don't get confused here. You think she'd bring you candy? And get this. The Intel Squad just came back from searching her tunnel under the old man's house. Inside was her folding-stock AK-47 and K-54 pistol. A K-54, buddy, a Russian officer's 9-millimeter automatic, black with a red star and 'CCCP' on the grip, nice leather holster too. She was definitely *not* just a messenger. She was—*is*—big-time, Communist Party member, VC village chief, and several other titles."

"Ngọc must be happy with the weapons," I say heavily. "More reward."

"Oh, yeah, he's got his fat finger deep in the pie."

I drive glumly through the heat back to Quảng Trị. Vinh sits silently smoking and pressed against the door, his long hair blowing in the wind. Suddenly he says, "I don't know why she said that. I've never seen her before. I don't know why she's VC."

"It's OK, Vinh, forget it."

"You don't think I'm VC, do you?"

"No," I say, focusing on the road ahead.

"I don't like the VC," he mutters. "If they win, they won't let me play my music, they won't let me wear my hair long."

"Vinh, drop it. I know you're not VC."

My mind reels with images of her crashing through the bamboo, swimming and lunging upstream, running up the ditch with my bullets making fountains all around her. I glance west to the mountains, where she came from, hiking through the wild forests of the Ho Chi Minh Trail, packed earth under her feet, AK-47 slung across her slim back, K-54 pistol swinging at her hip. Beside the road, sand dunes, parched fields, thatched houses stream by in waves. All I can think of is her.

Vinh stirs. "You know why she wouldn't take the gifts? It's not only because you're American and she's VC. It's not Vietnamese custom for a girl to accept gifts from a stranger. She doesn't know you."

"I want to know her," I say. *I want to know everything about her. I want to know where she gets the courage, the energy, the dedication. I want it for myself.*

I drop Vinh at his house, wind blowing across an empty porch and in waves through the young rice.

"One week!" Vinh calls from his flight toward the house. "I'll tell you when I find out about Lan's party."

"Thanks!" I call back.

I drive away with images of Lan's party forming in my mind, pretty Vietnamese girls in *áo dài*, soft drinks, Vietnamese sweets, and Vinh playing his guitar and singing with an unlit Marlboro behind his ear. Immediately visions of Annie come, her daring attempt to escape, then inside the wire of the District Compound, and locked in the terrible concrete cube with its battered table, pockmarked, stained walls, and caked-feces bucket in the corner, and I begin to weep for her and for my role in this, in putting her there, and for the continuing, nagging question: *What can be happening to her now?*

3

THE LOVE TEAM

It is the heart that counts.

— Hoàng Thị Nữ

I sweat through the week of Vinh's furlough. Lan's party comes, but I don't go. Early on the eighth morning I drive to Vinh's house. Young rice blows in the hot wind.

"Where to so early?" Vinh asks, smoothing down his sideburns as he gets in and checks himself in the mirror. "You missed a great party. I sang 'Love Potion Number Nine.' Everybody said it was great. Where are we going?"

I swing south on Highway One.

"Oh, no," Vinh groans, "not Hải Lăng."

"Only a few minutes, just a few questions."

Vinh stares out the side window, long hair caught by the wind. "I don't want to talk to her. She scares me." He pats his shirt pocket. "And I forgot my cigs."

"There's one behind your ear."

"Thank God." He pulls it out and taps it on his thumbnail. "Why do you want to talk to her anyway? She's not going to rally. And it stinks in there. I'll probably get sick."

I pull in through the wire of the District Compound and park near Rosie's office. He comes out, his big jowls shining with sweat.

"You're too late. She's been moved."

My heart sinks. "Moved where?"

"The PIK. Giang gave up on her. He never got farther than, 'I'm no one, just a messenger, just a woman.' He took her in his jeep. You probably passed them on the road. They put a shirt over her head."

The PIK! I think. The Province Interrogation Center, where high-level, hard-core VC are sent to be broken.

Rosie wipes his brow with his hand and flips big drops from his fingers. "She's out of our hands now, buddy."

"Not completely," I say.

"Don't think or do anything stupid," Rosie says. "Remember she *is* the enemy. She'd gladly put a K-54 round right between your baby-blues and laugh as you hit the ground. Whatever you're feeling for her, it's way out of line. Get real!"

"I just want to find out how she could do what she did, and what motivates her."

"Yeah," Rosie says. "Right."

I drop Vinh at the Chiêu Hội Center and drive to where the PIK sits by itself in a paddy just past the big ARVN base that guards the western approach to the city. Like the Hải Lăng dungeon, it's cube-shaped, concrete, and windowless. A narrow road on a dike connects it to the street, where there's a sandbag bunker and a young ARVN manning a barbed-wire gate. He follows me with his eyes as I drive slowly by, turn off on another paddy-dike road, stop, and look across the young rice at the PIK. A jeep is parked outside. Someone's in there with her.

Before I can stop it, a runaway train of crazy ideas takes off in my mind. I could break her out of there, set her free to go back to the mountains, go with her, renegades from both sides on the run. "Yeah, right," I hear Rosie say again.

Tears mix with sweat on my cheeks as I weigh my responsibility for this. If I hadn't gone to the Center on Wandering Souls Day, if I hadn't driven Ba and Đặng Sỹ down to Hải Lăng, hadn't taken them to Major Ngọc, hadn't driven Lúc-Thanh and the APT back for the operation. But there was no stopping me, or it. I was eager for adventure, eager for action. And now she was in there enduring who knows what.

Still beating up on myself, I drive back to the Center. Right away I feel something big is happening: no lookout on the watchtower, no guard in the sandbag bunker beside the gate. I get out and swing it open. The VC could walk in unopposed. No APT in tiger stripes and carrying assorted weapons lounging outside the barracks or in the shade of the headquarters. Even the South Vietnamese flag atop the big pole hangs limply, the mountain wind quiet for the moment. Then I hear it, music coming out of the middle barracks, multiple voices, and guitars.

Lúc-Thanh appears in the doorway, face flushed with excitement. "Cố vấn, come here! You've got to hear these two new ralliers, Ky and Lam. They were famous members of a VC Drama Team. Now they're with us!"

Not content with my slow pace and solemn look, he comes out, grabs my arm, and drags me to the door. The barracks is packed with APT. Even Vinh is there sitting among them and looking enraptured as two young men in VC clothes play and sing a traditional Vietnamese love song.

"Make way for cố vấn!" Lúc-Thanh shouts and he begins tossing APT aside the way big Sgt. Jones cleared the way to Annie lying on the infirmary table. "Sit here," Lúc-Thanh says and he plunks me down on a bunk nearest the singers, squeezing me in next to Đặng Sỹ, who, like the rest of the audience, looks lost in the song. From across the room, Vinh shoots me a glance, a grin, and a thumbs-up, then he, too, looks gone.

I gaze at the upturned faces and catch a few words of the

song: "Ancient village . . . rice fields . . . moonlight . . . country girl . . . sweet love . . ." The song ends and the room explodes with applause. APT are everywhere, jamming the doorway, looking in at the windows, packed on the bunks, sitting on the floor.

The VC could walk right in, I think. Maybe that's why this Ky and Lam rallied, get us to lower our guard, then . . . A scary thought hits: Maybe it's revenge for capturing Annie!

Gloom descends on me like a cloud. For a moment I was swept away by the music, too, and then came the thought of her.

Tall Đặng Sỹ rises and calls for attention, hand on the .45 slung low on his leg. "That's all for now. Ky and Lam have to rest. They've just come down from the mountains. Tonight, after dinner they'll put on a whole show. Invite your wives and children. Cố vấn, you come. Young brother Vinh, you, too, and bring the beautiful Miss Lan."

"I will!" Vinh shouts.

The APT slowly move out. Everyone's buzzing and glancing back at Ky and Lam, who look a little confused sitting at the back of the barracks with their guitars.

Vinh squeezes through the throng, joins me in my office, and sits under the big topographic map of the province. "I want to be their friend," he says excitedly. "We can make music together." He points at the green mountains all along the Laos border, dense with closely spaced brown contour lines of the Trường Sơn ("Long Range") Mountains. "Imagine, just yesterday they were out there, singing for the VC, and now they're here singing for us. Music unites us. It's about love."

"You think they're for real?"

Vinh looks surprised. "You think they're not? Their music is real. They're singing from the heart. You can tell. Did you go to the PIK?"

"I don't want to talk about it."

"Good, neither do I. Will you come tonight? I'm bringing Lan. She'll love it."

"Maybe."

"You need to get out more. You're thinking too much about the VC girl."

"I don't want to talk about it."

"Good. When will we interview Ky and Lam?"

"Tomorrow."

"I want to hear their stories. You know what? The APT are starting to accept me. You heard Đặng Sỹ called me 'Young Brother.' And he invited me and Lan."

"I'm glad . . ." My voice trails off, and I lose myself in the map, the green mountains and forests, home of the vast and secret Ho Chi Minh Trail: Annie's world. *Maybe Ky and Lam knew her. Surely, she's heard them sing. Tomorrow Vinh and I will ask them. I want to find out everything about her.*

Vinh and I work on the list of questions we'll ask Ky and Lam tomorrow. I don't include what I'll ask about Annie. At 5 o'clock I drop Vinh at his house.

"You better come tonight," he says. "You can learn a lot of Vietnamese words and about our culture from our songs. And Ky and Lam are *very* good. In peace, they'd be on the radio."

I smile. "Like you will."

He grins and closes the Scout door. "If peace ever comes."

"It will."

"But who will come out on top? If all the VC are like Miss Nữ, I'll tell you who will win. You know the first name 'Nữ' means 'Woman.'"

"Rosie told me."

"If her side wins, take me to America, me and Lan. I'll try my singing over there, in the land of the King, Elvis Presley."

"I'll do that."

"And show up tonight: 7 p.m."

I drive back to the PIK and park on the dike road looking across the young rice at the rolls of razor wire surrounding the windowless structure. Another jeep is parked outside and another young ARVN with an M-16 looks at me through the firing slit of his sandbag bunker. I sit low in my seat and think more crazy thoughts. To break her out of there I would have to kill at least two innocent people. Maybe she wouldn't accept my gift of freedom anyway, maybe she'd say, "Take it away" like she said about the foolish gifts I laid on the table at the Hải Lăng dungeon, or she'd use it as an opportunity to kill me, like Rosie thinks she would. *Like I deserve.*

I drive back to my room in the Agricultural Advisor's compound and lie on my bed. I don't feel like listening to Ky and Lam's sentimental love songs. I try to sleep and hope to dream of her, looking like Miss Moon and talking perfect English with that same charming British-Vietnamese accent. In my dreams she'll tell me the secrets of her power and courage. The clock ticks annoyingly on my headboard. I wrap it in a towel and bury it under a pillow. I toss and turn and finally sleep. I don't dream of her. She still fills my mind in the morning as I drive through the Center's gate and park by the big flagpole.

Chiêu Hội Chief Thuận, my counterpart, is back from his vacation. Thuận is tall and husky, a devoted husband and father of two cute girls. Like Vinh, he's a sometimes student at Huế University, his pursuit of an advanced degree in political science interrupted by the war. Also, like Vinh, he speaks excellent English and he uses this civilian government job to avoid being drafted into the ARVN, where he knows as an infantry second lieutenant, his life expectancy would be severely limited. Before I can dismount, his big beaming face appears in my open window.

"Cố vấn, this is the greatest thing! Have you heard Ky and

47

Lam? Come into my office. We've got a big plan going."

Vinh rolls up on his motorbike and parks in a cloud of dust.

"Good," Thuận says. "Bring Vinh in, too. He'll love this. He'll be part of it."

Vinh pulls back and looks suspicious. "Part of what?"

"Come," Thuận says, and he herds us into his office, where Ky, Lam, and Đặng Sỹ are talking excitedly around Thuận's big desk.

"Sit, sit," Thuận says in Vietnamese.

Ky and Lam immediately look wary. They're still wearing their VC black pajamas and rubber-tire Ho Chi Minh sandals, and now there are three non-ex-VC in the room. *Or at least one,* I think.

Thuận leans across his desk. "Ky, Lam, and Đặng Sỹ proposed it and I'm one hundred percent behind it. But it will take your support, cố vấn, big support, strong support."

As an advisor with access to cash, I've heard this line before. "That sounds like money. How much? And what for?"

Thuận gets up and sits close to me. "This is the plan. You're going to love it. Ky and Lam were the stars of a VC drama team. They traveled all over the province putting on shows for the people in villages at night—music, plays, comedy, all with the VC message, of course. The people loved it. They're starved for entertainment of any kind. Now with Đặng Sỹ they have this idea . . ."

As Thuận talks, I think, *Ky and Lam's rallying is related to Annie's capture. But how?*

Thuận pauses, then slaps my leg for emphasis. "We'll form our own Chiêu Hội Drama Team with Ky and Lam as the stars, but Vinh, too, with his guitar, and many APT can sing, act, do funny shows, and we hire more singers, pretty girls, too. Quảng Trị has many, and we show movies, too, buy generator, lights, the people in the villages have never seen anything like it."

Thuận pauses again. He's sweating and breathing hard. "And you know where we'll go, VC-controlled villages. With our message and our music. During the day, the APT will visit the VC families, persuade the mothers and fathers to get their sons and daughters to rally. At night, we'll put on our show. They'll love us for it. The country people have nothing to do at night but make babies."

Thuận bursts into laughter and Đặng Sỹ, Ky, and Lam look at him strangely, wondering what it's all about.

Lúc-Thanh comes in, his bad eye rolling, and says, "What's happening?"

Thuận tells him in a burst of fast Vietnamese and Lúc-Thanh grins, rubs his hands together, and says, "Very good!"

"What about the VC?" I say. "They're going to come to the show, too?"

"Listen to Lúc-Thanh," Thuận says, "when I ask him."

Lúc-Thanh listens and grins. "We'll ambush the VC and shoot them dead!"

My mind reels with the possibilities: drama-team shows in VC villages, APT ambushes at night. But the whole thing could have been cooked up in the mountains in revenge for capturing Annie, and we're jumping right into it.

"What about it, cố vấn? You can get the money? It will take a lot to make our drama team number one."

"I can get the money," I hear myself say. "No problem."

My feeling is the same as when we launched the operation to capture Annie. I had my reservations, but there was no stopping this train and I could already see myself out there learning from Lúc-Thanh how he planned to stop the VC from disrupting the show — by ambushing and killing them. Although I was the adviser, Lúc-Thanh and the other ex-guerrillas were the experts at war in the night.

"We need a name for the team," Vinh says.

"I already got it," Thuận smiles. "*Đoàn Tình Thương* — Love Team!"

Love Team?" I say "Shouldn't it be something stronger? It sounds weak."

"We'll bring love to the people," Thuận says in Vietnamese.

"And if the VC try to stop us," Lúc-Thanh grins, "we'll kill them."

Everyone laughs, Vinh a little nervously. I think, *I guess that's it. Love Team. But what is the connection to Annie? And are Ky and Lam false ralliers who are setting us up for a big kill?*

I drive to the MACV Compound and call Rosie. "What's the latest on Annie?"

"Still in the PIK. She's setting records there, for not talking. Giang's starting to believe she's only a messenger."

"What do you think?"

"I know who she is. You saw her story in my files. But she's not giving anybody up. She says no one helped her in the villages, she operated alone. No one gave their names in the mountains and she just carried messages that she didn't read and put them in a hollow tree. Giang sent the Intel Squad to the hollow tree and, of course, there was no message there. She says someone must have picked it up."

"What about the weapons?"

"She said an NVA officer in the mountains gave her the K-54 pistol because she's a woman and too weak to carry an AK, and she doesn't know whose the folding-stock AK was. Somebody else left it there. I'll tell you this: she's not weak."

"How long can she survive in the PIK?"

"Look, will you get off it? I told you she's out of our hands. They don't let me near that place. I gotta go."

I drive back to the Center and Thuận and I begin to finance the Love Team. With the flow of troops and supplies to Vietnam, there's also an immense river of money, and as a Refugee Advisor in Huế in '66 and '67, I had built schools, wells, refugee camps, and distributed tons of food. Supplying the Love Team with the best in electric guitars, a drum set, speakers, movie projector, generator, lights, banners, a Tri-Lambretta to haul supplies, and cash for Chief Thuận to hire three cute girl singers, and one disabled young man, whom Thuận assured me was the best singer of traditional love songs in the province.

All over the Center for days, under the direction of Ky and Lam, rehearsals are in full play, songs practiced, lines of skits learned, Vinh part of it all, but keeping his song or songs secret from me.

"He's almost like one of us now," Đặng Sỹ says playfully, as he and Vinh come out of the barracks, closely followed by Ky and Lam, now wearing the tiger-stripe camo of the APT.

"No, I'm not," Vinh says to me in English.

I marvel as I look at Ky and Lam. Just a few days ago they were traveling in the mountains and to the villages singing VC songs and promoting the VC line: "Americans out of Vietnam, Overthrow the Corrupt Puppet Saigon Government," and Ho Chi Minh's classic slogans, "Nothing Is More Precious than Independence and Freedom," and "Unity, Unity, Great Unity: Victory, Victory, Great Victory."

Now they were ostensibly with us, getting us ready to go back to the world where they had entertained. *Did Annie's capture set all this in motion? Would we only learn this when we were out there? Or in the next life, after they kill us all?*

In the morning, Thuận calls us to a conference around the flagpole. "Ky and Lam say we're ready, so today we go."

A surge of energy hits and everyone starts talking in fast

Vietnamese, waves of rising and falling sound.

Today, I think, *just like that? An American unit would take days of planning, briefings, logistical preps, coordination with other units . . . we've just been rehearsing the shows, and now we're going. But where?*

Another buzz of excitement comes as our new Tri-Lambretta rolls in with a cloud of dust, and three pretty girls in colorful *áo dài* and a young, disabled man in black pajamas get out and shyly approach our throng.

"Good!" Thuận says in Vietnamese. "The rest of our stars are here. All right, everyone, we leave in one hour. Get ready quickly. Đặng Sỹ and Vinh, watch over the new members of our Love Team!"

Everyone scatters for the barracks and Thuận says, "Come in my office, cố vấn. We have some final planning to do."

Final planning, I think. *What about the beginning?*

In his office, Thuận draws me to his big wall map. Unlike my map, which features my passion for the mountains and forests of the Ho Chi Minh Trail, Thuận's focus is on VC-controlled hamlets and villages, most of them in Hải Lăng District near the sea and along the old road the French called *La Rue Sans Joie,* "The Street without Joy," Annie's home territory.

Thuận rubs his chin and gazes at the map.

"Where are we going?" I ask.

"I didn't decide yet."

"Chief? We're leaving in less than an hour. You didn't decide yet?"

He pats my shoulder to calm me. "I know, it's hard for Americans to understand, but if I don't know, nobody can find out. And if the wrong person finds out, maybe we will be dead already."

I start for the door. "You've got a point there. I have to get a pack together."

RICHARD L. STEVENS

"Pack for two days," he says, "maybe three."

I hurry home in a whirlwind of excitement and throw together three days of C-rations, poncho, pistol, M-16, and extra mags. Who knows what we're going to encounter out there, wherever we're going.

I drive back to the Center, where a strange convoy is forming. First is the blue Tri-Lambretta with the *áo dài*-clad new stars and the black-pajamed "unusual" youth singer aboard, and a big banner with "Love Team" in Vietnamese flying from the back. Đặng Sỹ, with our new battery-powered bullhorn, sits crammed in front with Vinh. Next comes the dark green APT pickup loaded with heavily-armed APT, including two with Chinese-made RPD machine guns on top of the cab. The Chief guides me into line behind the pickup and a grinning Lúc-Thanh climbs in to ride shotgun with his AK sticking out the window, and six APT jam into the back. Ex-North Vietnamese Army soldier Phi, Thuận's driver, whom nobody trusts but the Chief, pulls the Chief's big maroon jeep in behind me. Finally, there's a big ARVN truck loaded with Love Team gear, musical instruments, and generator, flying another "Love Team" banner and crammed with more APT in assorted camo patterns and with several types of U.S., Russian, and Chinese weapons. *We're ready to go, but where are we going?*

Thuận comes out of his office looking sharp in his tailored khaki uniform with the Chiêu Hội emblem on his left breast, a bird flying from black to white over a flame. He passes me without a word, goes to the Tri-Lambretta, talks low to the driver, and then comes down the line, bending and looking like he's telling secrets to each vehicle driver. To me and Lúc-Thanh he says, "Cổ Luỹ."

"Cổ Luỹ?" I say. "I'm not familiar with it. Is it on the map?"

"It's the old name," Thuận says. "Very picturesque and

53

historic place. The lead driver knows the way. It's at the lower end of the Street Without Joy. Many VC families there."

The Chief puts on an almost comical, lugubrious face, "Oh, cố vấn, sad news. I cannot go. The Province Chief called. I have to go to an important meeting. I'll try to join you tomorrow. We'll do two shows there."

Again, I think, *an important person who knows where we're going, is* not *going.*

Thuận waves his jeep out of the line and the province truck rumbles up close behind me, its "Love Team" banner snapping in the wind.

"The Chief doesn't go," Lúc-Thanh says.

"No," I say.

"We don't need him," Lúc-Thanh says, and he pats the stock of his AK. "We'll take care of ourselves."

"Do you know Cổ Luỹ?" I ask.

Lúc-Thanh grins and his bad eye rolls. "I know it all," he says. "The Lâm Thủy Forest is there, the hideout of a famous VC guerrilla, Võ Công Đỗ. Maybe Đỗ will try to stop our show. His wife lives in Cổ Luỹ. It's downstream from where we captured Miss Nữ. The same river she jumped into, but bigger. Very nice place. You will love it."

"You think Võ Công Đỗ knows Miss Nữ?"

Lúc-Thanh looks at me, both his eyes steady. "It's all her territory out there. Everyone is under her, even Võ Công Đỗ."

"*Đi!*" Đặng Sỹ shouts through his bullhorn from the lead vehicle. "*Đoàn Tình Thương, mình đi!* Love Team, we go."

Slowly we start to move through the gate, then bump along the road to the Center, south past the Citadel's moat and wall, and east on the old dirt road to the sea, with dikes and paddies to left and right, small shrines, scattered graves, thatched houses, and water buffalo belly-deep in mud. Barefoot kids in raggedy shorts, girls in white *áo dài* and conical rice-straw hats, old men, and old women come out to the road as our dust cloud approaches and Đặng Sỹ works his new bullhorn. *"Đồng bào, đồng bào!* People, People! The Quảng Trị Chiêu Hội Love Team is on the move! Where will our amazing show be tonight? When will we come to your location? Music, movies, comedy, and drama! The Chiêu Hội Love Team is here!"

Two miles from the ocean, where the paddies begin to change to sand dunes, we turn south on Highway 555, the French Army's "Street Without Joy," another ancient dirt road going back to when local lords ruled from Quảng Trị Citadel, and later the Emperor and then the French from Huế — and now Annie's world. *The land,* I think as the dust flies, *how deep the roots of her family go here, her family and her love: the sacred land.*

His AK still tracking the roadside, Lúc-Thanh elbows me and waves his free hand from the green paddies on the right to rolling, salt-white dunes on the left sprinkled here and there with bushes, ironwood, and eucalyptus trees.

"Beautiful, isn't it?"

"Very beautiful."

"If I have to die today, I think, *"this is a beautiful place to do it."*

"Tell me about Võ Công Đỗ."

Lúc-Thanh grins and takes off on a long and lively ramble, most of which I don't understand. I get, I think, this much: "Đỗ is the long-time leader of an elite guerrilla group operating out of the Lâm Thủy Forest near Cổ Luỹ. His wife and young son live in Cổ Luỹ and we'll visit them later today. He won't rally. He's a real VC, like Miss Nữ. He may try to attack our show, but we'll ambush him if he tries. We'll also hunt him in his underground bunkers in the Lâm Thủy Forest. 'Capture alive' is not in the cards.

"No girl to worry about. Look!" he says, pointing his AK to

our right front. "See the treeline. That's the Lâm Thủy Forest. Soon we'll be in Cổ Luỹ."

Ahead of us, Đặng Sỹ stands tall in the lead Tri-Lambretta, blasting his bullhorn toward the long line of trees. "*Đồng bào, đồng bào!* People! People! The Chiêu Hội Love Team is here! Big Show tonight in Cổ Luỹ! Music, movies, comedy, dramas! Everybody come to Cổ Luỹ!"

"Đỗ knows we're here now," I say.

Lúc-Thanh laughs and stares at the treeline. "He knows *everything* in Cổ Luỹ."

The lead Lambretta turns onto a narrow dike road and we point west, directly toward the Lâm Thủy Forest. Far beyond, the Long Range Mountains roll along the western horizon. *Annie traveled at night from here to there,* I think. *What kind of epic journey was that, through ambush-filled country?*

We enter a dense stand of bamboo, and branches brush and scratch our sides as the road narrows to a tight tunnel. Then the river appears in flashes of blue and brown between the yellow and green.

"Miss Nữ jumped into this water," Lúc-Thanh says, "near here. But see how the river is bigger, wider. It's closer to the ocean."

Thatched houses appear on our left, surrounded by mango, papaya, coconut, and banana trees, and manioc and sweet potato patches. Kids peep from open doorways, but mostly the people are staying hidden as our convoy rumbles by and Đặng Sỹ keeps up a steady call: "Big Show tonight!"

Beside the river, the ruins of an old French-built church rise, in giant, scattered stones, all bullet-pocked and scarred by explosions. We pull into what was the church garden and park among charred tree stumps and big foundation stones. On a clothesline strung between two broken pillars, U.S. Marine camouflage pants and shirts hang drying and Marines doze in hammocks in the shade of the mango trees.

Great! I think. *A Marine Combined Action Platoon is here.* I'm immediately elated. It's a thirteen-man squad integrated with a PF platoon to try to prevent VC activity in and around the hamlet.

A shirtless, wiry, tanned Marine approaches me and extends his hand. "Corporal Slater, Commander of CAP Team Seven."

"Ex-Corporal Stevens," I say. "Semper fi. I've been out since '65. I'm the Chiêu Hội Adviser here."

"Civilian?" he says. "I can't wait. Hey, are all your guys ex-VC? We got radioed you were coming from Captain Rosenberg, District Intel. He's due here soon."

"Rosie's coming out here? All right!"

Slater's attention is suddenly caught by the Love Team girls squeezing out of the Tri-Lambretta. "Those are ex-VC?" he says. "Man, if I was Vietnamese, I'd join up."

"Not them," I say. "Most everybody else."

Slater shifts to the APT climbing down from the province truck with their assortment of weapons and camo uniforms. "And those are *ex*-VC?"

"Oh, yeah," I say. "For sure."

A jeep bumps slowly down the river road and Rosie gets out sweating and beaming. "I heard about this from Chief Thuận at the Province Chief's meeting. I'm going to be in the show. I couldn't miss this."

"You?" I ask. "You sing, dance?"

"I'm not saying. Wait and be surprised."

Slater gets even more excited. "Hey, Captain Rosenberg, come and meet my corpsman, Doc Johnson. He's an amazing singer and guitar player. The people love him here. He had his own group at Purdue. He's the skinny guy over there with the kids all around him."

They go off and soon Vinh joins them under a mango tree. Vinh calls Ky and Lam over and they all talk excitedly, with Rosie translating. I get the feeling this is going to be a really big event.

And what's going on here? I ask myself. *A week ago they would have met in a blaze of gunfire. Now they're talking music and Love Team.*

Slater comes back and joins me, and the APT begin setting up a stage in the church ruins. The Love Team girls pass us giggling, go down to the riverbank, and begin washing their hair. Beyond them on the water, six Marines in camo shorts on air mattresses are having an epic water fight with ten kids packed onto a half-submerged bamboo raft.

"Hey, take my rubber lady," Slater says, handing me his inflated air mattress. "I'd go in, but I've got radio watch. The river's mostly clean."

I look up and down the river. The brushy banks look like ambush heaven. "Seems pretty quiet here."

"So far, cool and quiet. We've got a great relationship with the people. Doc Johnson's cured all kinds of ailments and he's taught the kids prob'ly a dozen songs. We do night ambushes and daytime patrols with our PF Platoon and haven't had a contact in the two months we've been here. The VC have cleared out or are lying low. Hey go on, take a swim." He pinches the air mattress. "My lady knows the river."

I stash my pack behind one of the big stones, strip to my tiger-stripe shorts, and walk barefoot down to the river. A ramshackle bridge of floating barrels, long bamboo sticks, and rope crosses where the Love Team girls are still dipping their long hair in the water, and spreading straw mats in the lengthening shade of a huge mango tree.

"Cố vấn's going swimming?" one of them calls in Vietnamese.

They all laugh, and another shouts, "No way! Cố vấn's going

to play..."

I don't get the next two words, but they laugh as if it's the funniest thing ever.

"The Love Team Girls are Number One," I shout back in Vietnamese.

"No, cố vấn Numbah One!" they shout in English in unison.

I throw Slater's rubber lady in the water, jump on, and begin paddling for midstream, hoping the Love Team girls are watching.

Cute, vivacious, mischievous, sexy, and funny, I think. "They can sing, too," Thuận had said. *But they couldn't do what Annie did or endure what she's going through now.*

The current starts to take me past the big water fight, through a gap in the barrel-and-bamboo bridge, past a half-ruined temple, thatched houses, fruit trees, gardens, floating rafts of water hyacinths, and thick moss along the muddy bank.

Shrieks and shouts erupt behind me and I twist and look. The Marines' and kids' crafts have closed, with the kids swinging bamboo swords and the Marines rocking the kids' raft and trying to dump them into the river.

I give myself to the current again and slip into a dream-state of being a kid again and floating down the Des Moines River with my buddies, Lynn and Irv, on a raft we made, fishing and playing Tom Sawyer and Huckleberry Finn.

"Row, row, row your boat," starts playing in my head, especially the words, *"Merrily, merrily, merrily, life is but a dream."* I trail my hands in the slow-moving water and feel the rubber lady warming beneath me. What does that mean, *life is but a dream?* For a few moments I forget about ambush from the brushy banks and Annie being tortured. *"Merrily, merrily, merrily, merrily, life is but a dream."*

Something moves in the bamboo on the right bank, and I

instantly roll off into the water. Mostly submerged under the air mattress and peeping over it, I see it's a woman in a conical hat coming down to wash clothes on a flat rock at the river's edge.

I climb back aboard, and she smiles and waves as she begins to dunk, pound, and wring what look like VC black pajamas. Above her on the bank, a teenage local Popular Forces soldier with an M-16 slung across his back strolls along the riverside path, carrying a large green and yellow pumpkin. Suddenly I feel I know why Slater's CAP team has a quiet time here. The PF they partner with are from here, and so are the local VC. They're the grown-up kids playing in the water with the Marines. They don't *want* to meet in the night, and through family connections and kid-time friendships, they make sure they don't. Will we upset that balance?

The hamlet's last house along the stream slowly passes and reality hits in the heavily wooded banks ahead, and to my right, not far away across a fallow paddy, the dark and ominous treeline of the Lâm Thủy Forest. Võ Công Đỗ could have me in his sights right now and be thinking, "What's that balance-upsetter doing here, he and that bunch of filthy traitors?"

No more *merrily, merrily...* I swing my rubber lady around and begin stroking hard back toward the bridge, the Marines and the kids, and the Love Team girls stretched out and curled up on mats in deepening shade. Dripping, I climb the bank past them, and Cổ Hồng, "Miss Rose," long-haired, baby-faced, voluptuous, and the last to be hired, rolls on her side and calls out from her mat, "Was it fun?"

"Very fun," I call back.

She sits up and pats her mat. "Here is more fun," she says.

I keep walking but my heart is racing. Now what did she mean by that? I had met her just two days earlier when I found her in Chief Thuận's office crying, her round face streaked with tears and her braless breasts heaving. She was dressed in a jet-black *áo dài* and her gleaming black hair hung to her waist, where the split in her *áo dài* showed a triangle of golden skin.

"She's crying because she wants us to hire her for the Love Team," Thuận had said. "I told her we planned for three girls, and we had three already."

She had grabbed and squeezed my arm, pressing it against her, and unleashing a torrent of tearful Vietnamese.

"Can she sing?" I had asked.

"One of the best. Sometimes she sings on the radio from Huế. She's from Hải Lăng. Her father's a Village Chief there."

Annie's territory flashed in my mind. *What's the connection?*

Thuận had pulled me away from her and lowered his voice. "I have to tell you this. Some of the APT from Hải Lăng say she's a bad girl, if you know what I mean."

That baby face? That lush body? A bad girl?

"Isn't Chiêu Hội about forgiveness? The Love Team about love?"

"You're right!" Thuận had said. "If you have the money, she's on. She'll be a great addition to the show. I've heard her on the radio. Nice looking too, don't you think? Big for a Vietnamese girl."

I walk back to the ruins, where Rosie and Slater talk low in the church, sitting on cases of C-rations and leaning back against a broken wall painted with Hồ Chí Minh's slogan, "Nothing is more precious than independence and freedom." All around is Marine Corps gear, belts and packs, weapons, drying camo, and more cases of C-rations.

"Tonight's chow?" I ask, looking at Slater's seat.

"No way!" he says. "Mostly we eat with the people. We give them our C's; they make us great chow. How was the swim? Hey, this show is going to be great."

Đặng Sỹ, Lúc-Thanh, and tall, affable Nam enter the ruins with their weapons.

"Cố vấn, we're going visiting VC families," Đặng Sỹ says. "Want to come?"

I dress and grab my M-16. Outside the ruins in a whisper Lúc-Thanh tells me, "We're going to Võ Công Đỗ's house."

Lúc-Thanh leads us to the bridge, and we cross, making the barrels dance, the ropes groan, and the bamboo poles shake. An old woman washing clothes at riverside watches us, thinking, I guess, the same as me: *Any moment the bridge is going to toss us all in the water.*

We make it to the other side, then left on the riverside path past houses, the half-ruined temple, gardens, trees, and other paths branching from ours and headed across the paddy to the Lâm Thủy Forest.

Lúc-Thanh stops us and points with his eyes at a rice-drying yard where a small boy is playing near a poor-looking house.

"That's his son," Lúc-Thanh whispers.

Đặng Sỹ turns, grabs Nam's sleeve, and points at the boy. Nam nods and Lúc-Thanh leads us forward.

The boy looks up from the dirt where he seems to be drawing pictures. "*Má ơi!* Mom! People coming!" he shouts.

A woman's voice bursts from darkness inside the house. "Child, come here! Hurry up!"

The boy stands but doesn't move. He stares at us, especially me, entranced.

The woman shouts again. "Child! Come here!"

Lanky, smiling Nam walks over to the boy, while Lúc-Thanh leads Đặng Sỹ and me across the rice-drying yard to the open door. A worn-looking woman emerges from the dark interior, her bare, cracked feet on the packed-earth floor. She looks anxiously past us to where the boy is talking to Nam.

In formal Vietnamese, Đặng Sỹ introduces us. "Mrs. Đỗ, we're from the Quảng Trị Chiêu Hội Love Team. We invite you and your son to the big show tonight at the church after sunset. You're sure to enjoy music, comedy, and dramatic plays. We also invite you to persuade your husband to rally, as we all have. He'll get a big reward for himself and 5,000 *đồng* for every weapon he brings in. All the family will get a house in the Chiêu Hội Village outside Quảng Trị and he can qualify for joining the Armed Propaganda Team, like us. You can be together again with no fears of him being killed at night."

Mrs. Đỗ seems hardly to be listening but is more interested in her son's and Nam's interaction down by the river, where both are bombing floating sticks with dirt clods.

"Will you communicate that message to your husband?" Đặng Sỹ asks.

"I will, but I hardly see him."

"When was the last time?"

She cranes her neck to look past us. "Maybe two years ago. I don't know if he's alive or dead."

"How old is the boy?"

"He's four. Now if you don't mind, I have work to do. Child! Come in, now!"

"Thank you," we all say.

Nam joins us on the path. He's smiling.

"Well?" Đặng Sỹ asks.

"Instant friends," Nam says. "He's the same age as my boy."

"Well? Out with it."

"When I asked him if he sees his daddy now and then, he said not too much, but sometimes he brings me things. When I asked him when he saw him last, he said, 'Last night.'"

"He will come tonight," Lúc-Thanh says. "We'll put out ambushes with the Marines. Cố vấn will help arrange it. Đỗ will try to disrupt the show and make us look bad. He will never rally. He's like Miss Nữ."

We walk back, our boots thumping the riverside path and tree-shadows lengthening. I feel my heart thumping too: a big night is coming for sure.

Đặng Sỹ, Lúc-Thanh, and Nam are mostly quiet, only occasionally calling out to the houses and people we pass, "Big show tonight! Bring all the family! See you at the church at sunset!"

We cross the bouncing, swaying bridge and enter the church ruins. The APT discuss what they learned at Mrs. Đỗ's house and their ambush plans, much of it directed at educating me.

"Cố vấn," Lúc-Thanh says, "did you see the bundles of sticks tied with vines outside her door? That's firewood she gathers in the Lâm Thủy Forest. That vine grows there. Guaranteed she goes there daily and takes food to Đỗ and his men. Tonight, when it's dark she'll go again and take him information about us."

Đặng Sỹ pulls my sleeve. "Cố vấn, talk to the corporal. Tell him we want six Marines. We'll supply nine APT, the best at night ambush. Three teams, APT and Marines mixed. Three ambush positions, five men each, watching the routes from the Lâm Thủy Forest. Lúc-Thanh will choose the positions. The rest of the Marines and APT will guard the show. Ambush teams meet at the schoolhouse as soon as the sun drops behind the mountains. You understand?"

I think I got it all, though I wish Rosie was here.

"Understand," I say.

I find Slater handing off the radio to carrot-topped Lance Corporal Carter, I tell him the plan.

"That's three APT and two Marines on each team," Slater says. "You sure these guys are OK?"

I spread my hands palms up. "I pretty much always trust

them with my life."

"I guess we'll do the same," Slater says. "Marines! Gather 'round. Count off."

The Marines count off to twelve and look at each other uneasily.

"OK, odd numbers on night ambush," Slater says to a chorus of groans and sighs of relief. "The rest, show protection. Corporal Brown, you're in charge of the ambush teams. Take them now to the schoolhouse. You'll meet Mr. Stevens and the APT there."

Black Lance Corporal Dawson, an M-79 grenade launcher slung over his shoulder, comes up to Slater with an anguished look on his face. "Hey, come on Jimmy," he says. "I only got twenty-eight days, man. I'm too short to go on night ambush. Gimme a break, man. Put somebody else out there. And what about our PF? I don't see none of them going out. And these new guys are VC!"

"*Ex*-VC," Slater says. "All the PF are guarding the show and we did fair and square like always, luck of the draw."

"Luck o' the draw, shit!" Dawson says. "I only got twenty-eight days and you're sending me out there."

"Move it, Dawson," burly Corporal Brown says, and the six Marines, with M-16s, bandoliers of ammo, an M-60 machine gun, and Dawson's M-79, head down to the river.

I follow and we cross the bridge, green water turning black and ripples from the bouncing barrels and trembling sticks making little waves lap against the mossy and muddy shore. A child's bare footprint is pressed into the mud there and in the midst of mixed and roiling emotions, I suddenly feel a wave of nostalgia for being a kid again, looking for muskrat tracks and fishing for sunfish at Grandpa Stevens's pond and throwing dirt clods like Nam and Đỗ's son in Annie's river. Soon, with thoughts of her, I'm back in the war again with boots scuffing the riverside path, the soft jingle of gear, and lengthening, deepening shadows.

We pass the temple ruins on the left, and turn into a schoolyard, where two big mango trees flank a recently-rebuilt school building, tin-roofed and missing windows and doors. Nine APT materialize from the shadows, their mixed camo and assorted enemy weapons mingling strangely with the Marines' regulation gear.

Lúc-Thanh explains the plan and I translate, hoping I'm getting it right. Dawson continues to mutter, "Twenty-eight days and I'm gonna go on night ambush."

Bootsteps on the path. Rosie shows up sweating. "I figured you'd need me here."

Lúc-Thanh repeats, and Rosie translates word-for-word: "Three teams, two Marines and three APT in each. Cố vấn, you come with me. Team One, we'll go to the tree-island in the paddy between Mrs. Đỗ's house and the Lâm Thủy Forest. Team Two, Nam will lead it. Take the path behind the schoolhouse to the graves halfway out in the paddy and facing the forest. Team Three, Một the leader. The paddy-dike to the east that stretches to the forest."

We form up and move out. Ahead of our team is the dark tree-island, to the left is Mrs. Đỗ's house and to the right, the long and ominous Lâm Thủy Forest pointing toward where the sun has gone behind the Trường Sơn Mountains and the Ho Chi Minh Trail.

I walk behind Lúc-Thanh, Bốn, and Luân. They glide swiftly, silently, and totally focused. Behind me, I hear Carter's boots, breathing, and occasional soft, metallic sounds from the big M-60 he's carrying. Behind him, Brown, our "tail-end Charlie," pauses occasionally and looks back, making sure we're not being followed.

Lúc-Thanh angles for the tree-island. When we're under the overhanging limbs of the outermost trees, he calls us together and whispers. "Cố vấn, you and the corporal ambush here. Watch the path across the paddy. It's the one that comes from Mrs. Đỗ's house. Luân will lead the red-head Marine to the other side of the grove. They'll watch another path there that goes to the forest. Bốn and I will be at the shrine at the head of this grove, that's the reason the trees are here. We'll be closest to the forest and able to see both paths from there. You understand?"

"Understand," I whisper, and I translate to Brown and Carter as best I can.

With that, the APT and Carter are gone, swallowed by the trees, only a slight rustling and a branch twanging against Carter's M-60, then silence, wind in the trees, and from the hamlet, the first sounds of the show warming up.

"Let's crawl out in the grass a ways," I whisper. "We can see the path better."

"Good idea," Brown whispers.

A fringe of long, soft grass grows from the trees to the dry stubble of the paddy and we drop and crawl through it to just under the outmost reach of the overhanging trees. Brown lies with his M-16 ten feet to my right looking forward, watching the back of the hamlet and Mrs. Đỗ's house. I lie low, looking along the raised dike path from the hamlet to the broad tree-fortress of the Lâm Thủy Forest. Brown squirms around to get comfortable, crackling in the dry grass, and I begin to have misgivings about our position. Lúc-Thanh has taken the best position fronting the Lâm Thủy Forest. Plus, he has isolated me and Brown here, easy pickings if he, Bốn and Luân are VC. *Maybe all the APT on the ambush teams are still VC. Đỗ could come out of the forest, link up with Lúc-Thanh, and they could go on to wipe out the whole CAP Team, Rosie, Vinh . . . even Vinh! What did Annie mean when she said, "You know"?*

Brown can't seem to get comfy in the grass. If Đỗ's around, he'll hear us for sure. *Damn, he makes a lot of noise.* Suddenly, he's quiet. Thank God! Then I hear deep and regular breathing. He's asleep! We're only here a few minutes and he's already asleep. Isn't he afraid he's going to miss something? I debate whether to wake him and decide against it. At least he's quiet. I settle down and focus on the path, sweeping my eyes from the dark hamlet and houses to my right to the black woods to my left. I think about what I've learned from Annie. *I'm just a messenger*, she keeps repeating, and I begin to wonder what *is* her message, and to question whether we can win this war. For one, she's showed me what human beings are capable of, both in her physical feats and courage to try to keep us from capturing her, and what she's endured and *is* enduring to protect those who helped her, and to conceal her real role. Who do I know that could do that? No one. Not I. What then, does she have that we don't? To my right, Brown catches Z's. In the distance, Vinh, a little nervous, tests the sound system: "One-two-three-four. Testing, testing."

Annie's the most remarkable person I've ever met, I think. *She's in a category by herself. She's a super-hero, and I don't think we are going to win and maybe it's right that we're going to lose. But wait, the VC are not angels, not even close —*

I see someone! No, not someone, but a light, materializing out of the back of the hamlet, where trees and thatched houses blend in black, a light floating in the night sea, rising up on the dike path, and moving across my field of fire. I press myself into the earth and track the light with the black barrel of my M-16. Now I think I see, I imagine I see a human form, a field of energy around the light. I could shoot. Anyone out and moving after sunset curfew is fair game in the world of hunter and hunted. I could shoot, send a stream of hot metal out toward the light. But it's too far. I'd miss, the light would go out, our position would be known, and it might be Mrs. Đỗ. It probably *is* Mrs. Đỗ, on her way to tell her husband news of the show. I pull my finger away from the trigger but continue to track the light with my muzzle. Surely now Lúc-Thanh and Bốn see it too, as it nears the long black line of the Lâm Thủy Forest and is swallowed in it. I imagine Đỗ, his wife, and his men, squatting under the trees, talking in hushed tones, making their plans.

Silence, wind in the trees, Brown's regular breathing, more sounds of the Love Team tuning up, and then without warning all Hell breaks loose. Across the paddy, where the graves of Team Two's position rise above the dike paths, the flash-bang of an M-79 grenade sets off a maelstrom of automatic fire from M-16s and AK-47s, red tracers among the sheet-lightning flashes, all streaming toward and into the Lâm Thủy Forest. "What the ..." Brown says, as he jerks awake, rolls behind his '16, and tries to make sense, like me, out of the continuing flashes and hammering.

There's a pause and then beyond Team Two, Team Three opens up, more flashes, bangs, and streams of fire headed into the trees. It looks like both teams have been attacked!

Now our turn! I think. I swing my rifle to the left front, expecting to see VC crawling toward us out of the forest, maybe even Lúc-Thanh, Bốn, and Luân joining them.

"Cố vấn!" Lúc-Thanh, Bốn, Luân, and Carter come creeping through the trees and crouch with us in the grass while Lúc-Thanh whispers what he believes happened.

"First, an M-79 from Team Two, then they all open up. No return fire. The VC don't retreat back into forest, they shift to the east, still trying to enter the hamlet. Team Three sees them and everybody shoots. Again, no return. Maybe they killed some VC."

A big whooshing sound flies overhead, a "POP!," and a 105mm illumination round comes floating down under its little parachute, hissing fiercely and making giant shadows dance.

"Slater's calling in light from Hải Lăng," Brown whispers, and I remember the 105s ringed by barbed wire just beyond Annie's dungeon.

A crashing comes down through the trees just behind us, breaking limbs and stripping leaves, and then, as we dive and hug the ground, a big "THUD!" hits a few feet away. The first flare burns out and another "WHOOSH-POP-THUD!" comes, and falling limbs and leaves just behind us, sending us crawling out into the paddy.

Brown looks back where branches and leaves are still falling. "We're on the glide path of the illumination rounds. An empty canister hits you, it's all over, baby."

We crawl farther into the paddy and lie flat as round after round flies over and thousands of chemical candlepower turn night into strange day of giant, swaying, dancing shadows of trees, houses, graves, shrines, elevated paths, and armed men lying low and pressed to earth.

Finally, the big cannons cease firing and we lie in deep and vibrating black. Far out in the paddy, a green star cluster flare shoots up and quickly burns out.

"The signal to meet back at the church," Brown whispers. "Let's go."

Behind Lúc-Thanh, we weave a different route back to the bridge, cross it, and enter the church ruins. Rosie, Slater, Vinh, and the girls are there with anxious looks. Teams Two and Three arrive and pandemonium breaks loose, with everyone talking at once, telling their parts in the story. At first it reminds me of the crazy energy of a high school football team after a very big victory with everyone shouting at once, telling what they did.

Here, it's how they shot and what the VC did. As I begin to understand it, I see the APT, especially of Team Two, are pissed.

"He did it!" they say, pointing at Dawson. "The black Marine! He shot too soon. Way too soon! The VC were coming right for us. We told the Americans, wait till they're *this* close." Một puts his hand in front of his face. "We would have killed every one of them! They had no idea we were there!"

Team Three chimes in with their story. "After Team Two started shooting, the VC came running in our direction. They were still trying to get into the hamlet. We might have hit one."

"Shit!" Nam says, glaring at Dawson. "We could have got them all."

"Slater," Dawson pleads, "I *told* you not to send me out there. I'm too short to get hit now, man, an' the Charlies was comin' right for us. There was a bunch of 'em, too."

"You know what, Dawson?" Slater says, putting his hand on Dawson's shoulder and looking him in the eye. "You're right. I never shoulda sent you out there and I won't again."

"Enough of this," Rosie says. "We've got a show to put on and protect. And we need to call the people to come."

He unleashes a torrent of Vietnamese and Đặng Sỹ and Lúc-Thanh order the APT into furious action, while Slater does the same for the Marines. Soon the church is cleared except for the performers and me, and people are starting to filter into the churchyard, drawn by the humming generator, lights burning over the stage, and Ky and Lam with bullhorns going up and down the riverside path calling the people as they had to VC drama-team shows.

Behind the big stone with the VC graffiti, Rosie digs his elbow in my ribs. "I'm glad you had to come back in. Now you can see what I'm going to do in the show."

"I hope Võ Công Đỗ's not going to be in the audience," I say.

"He might not like your act."

"You know, your APT came close to wiping out a major part of the VC presence in Hải Lăng. With them losing Annie, and if they would have lost Đỗ and his men, too, it would have been a big blow to them here. And Hải Lăng is the key to both Quảng Trị and Huế."

More people, kids, young girls, and oldsters arrive, and begin sitting on benches the APT and Marines carried from the school.

"Đỗ will still try something is my bet," Rosie says. "He can't let this go unchallenged in his own territory, especially after losing his chief, Miss Nữ."

"I'm afraid to ask. Is she still—"

"Sent to the Province Hospital, VC Ward. They gave up on her in the PIK. She convinced them she's just a messenger. But she's in bad shape. Giang told me."

I can visit her there! I think. I'll take her what she needs to get well. I'll get to talk to her again!

"I see it in your face, buddy," Rosie says. "Jewish-Swami sees all and knows all. But we've got a show to do here first and there's no guarantee it's going to get through without a visit from Mr. Đỗ. You need to be totally *here*."

A drum roll comes from the stage, the big new bass drum a-pounding, and then a fast riff from the snares, our gaudy new set. The curtain opens. It's Vinh! He waves his sticks and grins.

"He's good, you know," Rosie says. "He told me this would surprise you. He wants to drum for all the musical numbers except his, when he'll play guitar and sing."

"Life is full of surprises," I say.

"Let's hope tonight's are all pleasant ones," Rosie says.

The three original Love Team girls pass by and wriggle onto a bench up front, holding each other and giggling. Cỏ Hồng sits a little apart. Even farther is young Chinh, the disabled singer.

More people come in, filling the school benches, and perching on the church's foundation stones.

"Looks like it's going to be a good crowd," Rosie says. "I'm going to grab a seat up front while the grabbin's good. Watch for my act. It's showtime!"

"Sounds like a New Yorker's philosophy of life," I say. "Is 'Captain Rose' going to sit up there with 'Miss Rose'?"

Rosie grins. "Well, there is a little space between her and the rest of the girls."

"You need a bigger space than that, buddy. Better try one of those big stone blocks."

"What about you?"

"I'm gonna stand, move around, watch out for Đỗ."

Rosie turns to go. "Just don't miss my act."

"Not for the world," I say.

Gripping my M-16, I melt into the darkness beyond the circle of light from the bare bulb hanging over the stage—the way the bare bulb hung over Annie in the infirmary. I watch the people come, and bulky Rosie weave his way among them, rapping in Vietnamese, laughing, and, sure enough, stopping at the small space between curvy Cổ Hồng and to her right, tiny, cute, and well-named Cổ Lạc, "Miss Peanut." Hồng looks up and bumps with her ample butt the hamlet kid to her left, making enough space for Rosie to plop down next to her. Whatever it is he's saying, everybody around him is laughing like crazy.

Onstage, Vinh continues to riff the drums, and Ky and Lam climb up, take two shiny new electric guitars from their stands, and begin tuning them to the delight of the crowd. *If the energy is this high just for tuning up, what is it going to be like for the show?*

The churchyard is now packed, with all the benches and stones jammed, and people standing, half-in and half-out of the circle of light, and a few like me in the darkness. Đặng Sỹ, looking sharp as usual in tailored tiger-stripe camo, beret cocked to one side, and big .45 pistol hanging to his knee, mounts the stage and grasps the hanging mike.

"People of Cổ Luỹ," he says. "Welcome to the Quảng Trị Chiêu Hội Love Team Show! You'll hear heavenly music, see heart-gripping drama, and laugh yourself crazy at side-splitting comedy. So, now, to take you to that heavenly place, the singing of Lý-Chinh!"

Vinh starts a long drum roll and I think, *No, not Chinh, don't start with him!*

Chinh is the handicapped 19-year-old Thuận insisted on hiring, though I'd seen the lack of respect, even terrible treatment, he got from the kids around the Chiêu Hội Center, and I was sure village kids would do the same. Đặng Sỹ from below and Ky and Lam from above help Chinh onto the stage and position him under the mike. His withered left arm is tucked into the pocket of his Love Team shirt, his spine is slightly twisted, and he has a small humpback. A wisp of hair hangs over his thin face and his eyes repeatedly cross and uncross in a strange jerky dance. The kids in front shriek as if they're seeing a monster, and he winces as if hit with blows as I saw him do while walking to the Center with a crowd of jeering kids behind him.

"But he can sing," Thuận had said.

Just don't start with Chinh, I think again, as he shakily reaches up with his one good hand for the microphone, and smiles his shy, hurt smile. *Just don't start with Chinh,* I think again as the kids whoop, jeer, and laugh.

Ky, Lam, and Vinh play the intro to a classic Vietnamese love song, Chinh begins to sing, and the jeers immediately go silent. I see, we all see, something miraculous, the transformation by music of infirmities to power. Chinh's voice is rich and glorious and he sings of love as if he lives it, is *made* of it, and there's more. He's physically transformed, *healed* by singing. He stands straight, full-chested, his spine straightened, his hump gone. His eyes don't dance, his face glows, he's *beautiful*. I take a fast glance at Rosie and the girls—they're enraptured. We all are. We're seeing a miracle. I begin to weep and am glad I'm standing in the dark.

The song ends and the crowd goes wild with applause and cheers. For a moment Chinh basks in it, then a confused look appears on his face, and he begins to transform back again. Ky and Lam help lower him off the stage and Vinh drags the curtain closed, a white sheet with "Love Team" in Vietnamese and the Chiêu Hội emblem, the bird flying from dark to light over a flame. The crowd murmers in anticipation. We're all lit, and I realize that for a few moments in Chinh's song, I forgot all about Đỗ and what he might do, even about the visit to Annie as soon as I get back to Quảng Trị.

Something is happening onstage behind the sheet-curtain. I see the boards bending and hear kids' muffled laughter. The curtain opens and there's Doc Johnson, the Marines' Navy corpsman and Cổ Luỹ's "doctor," sitting on a chair with his guitar across his lap and ten of "his kids" around him. Vinh hits the drums and Johnson swings into a rousing version of "This Land Is Your Land," with the kids joining in on "This land is made for you and me" at the top of their voices. The people love it.

The curtain closes. More dancing and bouncing of the boards, and Vinh nervously clearing his throat. The curtain opens and now it's Lam on the drums, Ky and Doc Johnson on backup guitars, and Vinh under the mike with his guitar, hair slicked back, and tight jeans on. Cổ Hồng leads a "woo-hoo" that the hamlet people join in, and Vinh grins and strikes one of his much-practiced Elvis poses.

"*Đẹp quá!* Very beautiful!" Hồng shouts.

"*Đẹp!*" Rosie echoes, laughing, and the Love Team girls take it up almost like a chant. Vinh looks like he's in heaven.

Here comes "Love Potion Number Nine," I think, and Vinh glances back at Doc, Ky, and Lam, snaps his fingers, counts, "One-two-three," and they swing into a big surprise, the Beatles' "Ob-la-dee-ob-la-da, life goes on, bra, la-la, how the life goes on . . ."

I'm grinning from ear to ear, lost in the joy and energy of the crowd, and the memories of the many times I've heard this song. Surely few if any of the villagers understand a word of the song and in fact, though Vinh's spoken English is excellent, he's running together the already obscure lyrics about "Desmond . . . marketplace . . . Molly . . . singer in the band." But it doesn't matter. Just as Chinh's song communicated "love" whether we Americans understood the words or not, so Vinh transmits "joy," and the old folks, young folks, girls, and boys have the same crazy grin that I do. "Ob-la-dee-ob-la-da, life goes on bra, la-la how the life goes on."

Cổ Hồng jumps up squealing and clapping. Rosie joins her and people all over the churchyard rise and join the applauding and whooping. Vinh looks like it's the best day of his life.

The curtain closes and there's more deep-bouncing boards as chunky Rosie climbs onstage and disappears behind the curtain. Muffled voices and the curtain opens on Vinh back on drums, Ky and Lam with their guitars, and a beaming, rotund Rosie, his jowls shining with sweat through his 5 o'clock shadow, and a goofy look on his face letting us know we're in for comedy. He glances back at the band, and they swing into "Auld Lang Syne."

"*Auld Lang Syne,*" I think. *What is this?*

The audience knows, though, for they start whooping and laughing right away as Rosie sings in Vietnamese a funny

76

children's song about the Phantom jumping in, a lizard losing its tail, and the French "losing their souls," and what makes it wildly hilarious is Rosie's grimaces and gesticulations, and that an American even *knows*—and can sing—this song. *Oh, how I envy him. Where does he learn this stuff?*

The show goes on with act after act, and even though I keep looking around at the edge of darkness for Đỗ to appear, I feel in a kind of dream-state, like the war is over and we're all here just having fun. The Love Team girls each sing one solo and one song together, and we all probably fall in love with them. Ky and Lam—amazing, dynamic actors—star in two plays they adapted from their VC drama team days, just switching the bad guys from the Saigon government and the Americans to the VC. There are two short films with the sheet as a screen, and the finale, a comedy about two bumbling VC in which the girls play, too, sends the people away laughing and buzzing with joy.

The lights go out and things get serious again. Đặng Sỹ and Lúc-Thanh materialize out of the night, followed by Một and Nam.

"We'll move across the river to the temple," Lúc-Thanh says. "Đỗ may try to attack us here."

I visualize us in a long line slowly crossing that bouncing, swaying bridge.

"Lúc-Thanh," I say. "No good! We'll be perfect targets on the bridge."

"Don't worry," Lúc-Thanh says. "We're not crossing the bridge. We're going by boat."

Lúc-Thanh leads us along the riverbank and down to water's edge where four woven-basket boats lie overturned on moss and mud. We flip them over and cross in a flotilla, pushing with long bamboo poles, black water lapping softly against bottom and sides. We climb the bank and follow the riverside path to the temple, where Lúc-Thanh sets the defenses around it and Đặng Sỹ leads the rest of us inside. On the temple floor and in the courtyard, we spread mats, blankets, and ponchos, whisper softly, and try to sleep.

Stars over the courtyard and mosquitos in my ears: I wrap up in my poncho with my M-16 lying beside me. Whispers finally cease. *Will Đỗ find us here?* Across the courtyard I see Cổ Hồng sitting upright on her mat, hair falling to her hips and a guitar across her lap.

Suddenly, "Twang-twang." She begins discordantly strumming the guitar. *What is she doing, signaling Đỗ?* "Twang-twang." *Not only signaling, but how can anybody sleep?* "Twang-twang."

I sit up, grip my rifle, and crouch over to her.

"*Chào, cố vấn,*" she says, and she uncrosses her bare feet and scootches over to make room on her mat. "I'm learning to play the guitar. Want to help me?"

"*Cô Hồng,*" I whisper. "*Tôi muốn ngủ.* I want to sleep. Please don't practice now."

"Okay," she says, and she puts the guitar aside, lies back, stretches out, and snuggles into the mat, hair falling over one side of her face. "I hope cố vấn sleeps deliciously."

"You, too," I say.

"I *always* sleep deliciously," she says, looking up at me with her one uncovered eye.

I crawl back to my poncho with my head reeling.

Suddenly, an explosion rocks the temple, followed by two bursts of automatic fire. We all scramble for cover. I run and dive into bushes just off the path and lie pointing my rifle toward the river.

Lúc-Thanh goes crouching down the path, comes back, and whispers to Đặng Sỹ, then me. "Một saw someone look over the

78

riverbank and start toward the temple. He threw a grenade and fired. We didn't find any blood trails. We'll look again in the morning. There may be a tunnel opening there. Đỗ knows where we are now."

I try to stay awake. Something splashes in the river. I plunge into sleep. At 4 a.m. a rough hand shakes my shoulder. It's Lúc-Thanh.

"Cố vấn, we're going into the Lâm Thủy Forest to hunt for Đỗ. Just APT, no Marines. Want to come?"

I stand and see APT lined up on the path. Lúc-Thanh inserts me midway into the line. It's the most experienced and most trusted APT, the same ones who went after Annie. Luân, who's from here, leads us weaving through a bamboo grove, into a sunken paddy, and directly to the Lâm Thủy Forest. There, under the dark trees and all without words, Luân and Lúc-Thanh peel three and four APT off at a time and vanish into black to place them in interlocking ambush positions. Luân takes Một and Bốn from in front of me, comes back without them, then guides me to the base of a large bush, pulls me down, and points to a space between two trees, my field of fire, my kill zone. With gestures he tells me that I am to shoot there and there only, and then he disappears to place the last teams.

Silence. Breathing and insect songs; soft stirrings in the grass. I feel utterly alone, like the only person in the world. I focus on the space between the two trees, slight silver-black between deep black. Is it a trail? The entrance to a tunnel, passage to another world? Was Cố Hồng's discordant playing a signal? Was the VC who poked his head over the riverbank a response? Was baby-faced, "bad girl" Hồng part of Annie's large and complex team out here, too?

The space becomes more silver, the trees less black. I begin to see the world around me, not the primal forest I imagined at a distance, but a large, destroyed village being reclaimed by the forest. All around are foundations and semi-walls of long-gone houses, heavily overgrown with vines and trees, former paths now a tangle of tall, dense grass, shrines sprouting bushes, fruit trees gone wild but still producing, wildflowers blooming, bird songs greeting a slow dawn.

Now I see my ambush partners Một and Bốn lying low in the bushes and grass, focusing on their spaces among the trees and interlocked with mine. Again, I marvel at the genius of Lúc-Thanh and the other APT, choosing just the right places to form a kill zone and also so we don't shoot each other.

Daylight: the VC won't be moving now. Lúc-Thanh emerges out of the green with the rest of the team. We form into a line and head back toward the hamlet on a different route. From the tight discipline of our night movement, the APT seem way too casual now, as if there's no possibility of encountering the VC. Several have gathered wild fruit and wildflowers, I'm guessing destined for the Love Team girls.

We approach the river and Cổ Luỹ and I feel for me the operation is over. I want to get back in time to visit Annie today. I have in mind different gifts than the foolish ones I took before and a way I think she'll accept them.

Three armed figures wait for us on the riverside path. It's Đặng Sỹ, Rosie, and Slater; they don't look happy.

Đặng Sỹ begins pouring out dire news to Lúc-Thanh while Rosie tells me the same.

"The VC killed an old man last night at the downstream end of the hamlet. A rumor is going around that the APT did it. We're going there now."

We hike fast on the path downstream. I question Rosie between steps and breaths. Cổ Luỹ's alive with morning sounds and smells and people heading down to the river.

"Who's saying the APT did it?"

"My guess is the VC, probably the same ones who killed him."

"Why him?"

"He was a low-level agent for Giang. Passed us information like, 'The VC came last night to collect rice,' or 'They gathered the people in the hamlet to talk about the revolution.' Nothing big. He made a few *đồng* for it. The VC probably knew about him for a long time. But they chose last night to kill him."

A woman is wailing ahead. We quicken our pace and turn off the path into a rice-drying yard. More wailing and moaning comes out the open door of a small, poor house. Two children stand outside, looking like they're in deep shock.

Đặng Sỹ and Lúc-Thanh go inside the house. The wailing intensifies, then abates. We hear multiple voices, male and female. Through the door we can see several people standing, a body laid out on a bamboo bed, and a woman in hysterics, throwing herself upon the body, as if to inject her life into it.

Đặng Sỹ and Lúc-Thanh come out and lead us back to the riverside path.

"The story is this," Đặng Sỹ says. "They were going to the show but felt afraid. The children begged and they changed their minds. As they were getting ready, two men came into the rice-drying yard and called the old man's name. He was afraid but he went out. A third man appeared and shot him in the chest with an AK-47. The wife saw it all from the door."

Một comes running toward us. Breathless, he pours out more news. "Another man was killed last night at the upstream end of the hamlet. Again, the rumor's going around that the APT did it."

We set off at a fast pace for the upstream end of the hamlet. Một leads us to another small, thatched house. More wailing inside, and a woman's anguished words, "Why did they kill him? He was seventy-two years old! How will I live? I don't even have a buffalo!"

We see through the open door an old woman circling a body laid out on a wooden table, pausing to dig her fingernails into the wood, and wailing as if to shake the house down.

Rosie goes in with Đặng Sỹ, and they talk to two old women who alternately stand in a corner out of the way of the widow's gyrations, and then pull her off her husband's dead body when she throws herself on it. They come out and we quickly move away from the house.

"Years ago, he was in the People's Self-Defense Force organized by the government," Rosie says. "I don't know if he was currently passing information to us. Giang doesn't share all his sources with me, and I don't share all mine with him."

"He was seventy-two years old!" the woman wails again from the house. "Why did they have to kill him?"

"Same M.O.," Rosie says. "Two men came during the show. They called him out by name, and a third man appeared and shot him in the chest."

"Do you think it was Võ Công Đỗ?"

"Him or on his orders," Rosie says.

"Because we were here," I say.

"Because we were here," Rosie says glumly. "Đỗ couldn't let that challenge go unanswered, especially after the almost-ambush we sprang on him. The VC have shown once again: we can't protect the people."

We hike back on the riverside path to the church, load up, and start driving up the Street Without Joy toward Quảng Trị. My mind is swirling with unanswered questions. *If Annie would talk to me, she could answer them all.* And Rosie's words haunt me: *"Because we were here." Would these two old men still be alive if we didn't come to Cổ Luỹ? If we didn't come to Vietnam, would*

Annie never have been wounded, captured, and tortured? If we didn't get involved, would four of my best friends, all killed in Vietnam, still be alive? Staff Sgt. "Goat" Hogan, Dwight Owen, Tom Gompertz, Nguyễn Văn Biển ? Would they still be alive? If—

Vinh's voice cuts into my thoughts. "Did you like my song?"

"What?"

Sitting by the window, hair whipping in the wind, he lights up a Marlboro. "Did you like my song? You didn't tell me yet."

I try to come back to here. "I loved it. I was surprised. I thought you would do 'Love Potion Number Nine' or an Elvis song."

He blows a big puff out the window. "I like the words, 'Ob-la-dee-ob-la-da, life goes on, bra, la-la how the life goes on.'"

I feel a sudden rush of something powerful, almost overwhelming, something rushing up from deep in my gut, flowing from my heart, racing up and down my spine, and bursting out in a flood of tears.

"Are you okay?" Vinh asks. "What is it?"

I wipe the tears from my cheeks. "I don't know—it's . . . life."

"Maybe it's love."

"Maybe it is."

4

TOMBSTONE SHADOW

Time to weep over our losses has gone. What's now
important is the present.

—Hoàng Thị Nữ

I DROP VINH off at his house, drive to the MACV PX, and load up
on bottles of vitamin pills and insect repellant. I pull up to my
gate and old Huynh slings his carbine, comes out of the sandbag
bunker, salutes, and drags the gate open, gouging the street. I
park, jump out, and start stripping off my clothes as I head for
my door. Fast shower, stash my weapons, dress in civvies, and
back out to my Scout.

I take the river road to the hospital, park in the compound,
hail a passing nurse, and think how to frame the question in
Vietnamese.

"Excuse me, Miss, where is the Việt Cộng house?"

She gives me a strange look. "Việt Cộng house?" she asks.

I don't know the word for "ward." I think, *I wish Vinh was
here.* I try again. "Wounded Việt Cộng, where?"

"Ah," she says. She points to a concrete building on the slope
to the river.

Grabbing my bag, I head for the door. Just inside, a young
ARVN sits in a long hall with an M-16 on his lap.

"What do you want?"

"I'm the Chiêu Hội Advisor. I want to talk to Miss Hoàng Thị

Nữ."

"I don't know their names," he says. "You'll have to go inside their room."

He leads me down the hall, unlocks a door, opens it a crack, and quickly steps back. A horrendous smell pours out of the room, so sickening it almost makes me retch. I feel it coating me, invading my lungs, filling my eyes, saturating my clothes. I try not to breathe, I wipe my eyes, and open the door wider. The room is packed with people standing, sitting, staring, slumped against the wall, lying three and four to a bed on four cots jammed against the far wall. The smell hammers me, and every instinct is to flee. Hollow eyes stare at me and wounded and diseased bodies begin to press toward the door.

"Don't come out!" the guard shouts at them from down the hall, and he brandishes his M-16. "Don't pass the open door!"

Those nearest the door move back in a wave and continue to stare at me with lifeless eyes. I see Annie and my heart breaks. She's packed in a mass and looks terrible, barely alive. An unbelievably dirty bandage circles her head. Her face is swollen, her body shrunken, her pallor ghastly, her eyes hollow and black-circled. She looks older, as if some doomsday machine has sucked years out of her. No one is young here. I see untreated wounds, malaria, raging dysentery, imminent death.

I hold up the bag and choke out in Vietnamese, "It's for the others." I reach over outstretched hands and pass it to her. "Vitamins and mosquito repellent: it's for the others. I'm going to try to help them."

She takes the bag and others crowd around her. I beat a fast retreat down the corridor, past the guard, out the door, and to my Scout. I breathe deeply and try to expel the stench, disease, wounds, horror. *She took the gifts! And now I know what I have to do.*

I look at my watch: 5:15 p.m. The docs will be in their room, getting ready for chow. I drive to the MACV Compound. The sign on the docs' door says, "MILPHAP: Military Public Health Assistance Program." Doc Lane is a Navy surgeon. Doc Symonds is a civilian G.P. from Nebraska. Both volunteered for MILPHAP to help the overwhelmed Vietnamese medical system. After a usually busy day in the Province Hospital, they're chillin' before chow in their air-conditioned room. We're friends. Doc Lane, slim and Navy-sharp, opens the door. Doc Symonds, tall and with a drink in his hand, looks over Lane's shoulder.

"Woof, where have you been?" Lane says, wrinkling up his nose.

"Hell," I say. "Better step outside. I don't want to contaminate your palatial quarters. I want to tell you something and I want to ask you something. First, did you know there's a VC 'ward' in the Province Hospital? It's a windowless room on the slope near the river. Maybe thirty or forty men and women are packed in there together. Four cots, no sanitation. People are dying. Maybe some were dead. It's horrific. Think Auschwitz."

They look at each other. "We did not know this," Lane says.

"We'll check it out tomorrow morning," Symonds says. "We're meeting the Director at 0800. We're getting him a shitload of new equipment, so we've got leverage. We'll have him take us there."

"There's a woman I'd especially like you to look at," I say. "She has a bandage on her head that has been there for probably two weeks, and she's been heavily tortured. Her name is Hoàng Thị Nữ. She's the Vietnamese Annie Oakley."

Lane gives a sly smile and looks like he would dig me in the ribs if I didn't smell so bad. He shoots a knowing look at Symonds and then back at me. "And your interest is?"

Tears fill my eyes before I can stop them, and I say with difficulty, "I helped put her there."

They get serious and Lane says, "We'll do what we can for her."

"For all of them," Symonds says, raising his glass. "That's what we're here for."

In the morning, I go to the Center. Lane and Symonds will be meeting with the Director now. Vinh is already in the APT barracks, rehearsing with Ky and Lam for the next Love Team show. He comes to my office and sits on my desk, swinging his leg.

"Did you see the new rallier? He came in last night from the mountains. His name is Xuân."

"Let's talk to him."

Vinh brings in a short, pale young man in VC clothes. He looks tired, malnourished, and scared. We sit around my big desk and Vinh fires off the usual first questions: name, position in the VC, and why did you rally?

As Vinh knows, I'm eager to get to questions about the Ho Chi Minh Trail, especially can you point out its location on my wall map? Before answering the stock questions though, Xuân unleashes a torrent of fast Vietnamese in which I hear "Miss Nữ... captured... very sad."

"Vinh, we didn't ask him anything about Miss Nữ. Why did he volunteer that info, start by talking about her?"

Vinh asks and translates the answer. "He said it was an important event that happened recently and that we would want to know."

"That they were very sad? Why?"

"Because she was very important and has a lot of sensitive information, including the names of many VC and supporters."

Xuân begins to answer other questions. He was a VC for five years, a nurse. He worked at a secret hospital in the forest. He rallied because he missed his home and family, and because life in the mountains was hard, especially at the hospital. Often, they had no food or medical supplies, not even bandages. They had to use wild plants."

"Ask if he knew Miss Nữ, and what were her positions."

The answer comes back. "He knew of her and that she had many titles and did many things. He doesn't know what exactly."

I look up at my big wall map. "Ask him to show us where was his hospital and what he knows of the Ho Chi Minh Trail."

"He says he only knows it on the ground, not on a map. He says it's very confusing out in the forest, and that he grew up in the city. It's not his world out there."

"Ask him if he can sing or play music."

"He says he's a pretty good singer."

"Tell him about the Love Team."

My phone rings. It's Doc Symonds. "You can visit her tomorrow. She and the other VC will be in Ward B. It's not Johns Hopkins, but it's better than that hell you told us about. We were shocked, and we've seen a lot."

I feel a wave of joy. "Thanks to you both."

"Lane did some minor surgery on her ear. It was pretty badly infected."

"I owe you a night on the town, spicy chicken soup at that little café on the river."

"Make it sooner rather than later."

"You look happy," Vinh says as I hang up.

"Tomorrow, we go to the hospital."

Vinh abruptly stands up. Xuân looks surprised.

"No, no," Vinh says, "Not to see Miss Nữ. She's sure to be in a dungeon. I can't handle that."

"No, she's in a good place. American doctors are taking care of her."

Xuân seems to be listening to us.

I ask him, "Do you speak English?"

"No, nothing at all," he says.

"What do you think, Vinh?"

Vinh studies him. "I don't think he's a nurse. And maybe he knows what I'm saying right now."

"Tomorrow at eight," I say. "I'll pick you up here. It will be very different than the first time, you'll see."

"May I go now?" Xuân asks.

"Introduce him to Ky and Lam," I say. "See if he can sing, and if they want him on the Love Team."

"The 'Singing Nurse'?" Vinh says. "I tell you there's something funny about him and it's related to Miss Nữ. He was too eager to tell us about her, like that was part of his mission."

In the morning on the road to the hospital, Vinh fidgets and smokes. "I'm going to quit, you know. Lan wants me to."

"I'll believe it when I see it."

"I can do it. For her." He takes a long, hard puff right down to the filter, and throws it out the window. "I don't know why you want to talk to Miss Nữ. She's not going to talk to us."

"Wait and see."

He scratches his sideburns and slumps down in his seat. "I hope she doesn't say, 'You know' again. I don't know what she meant by that."

We park in the hospital compound and go looking for Ward B.

Vinh glances down at my PX bag. "What's in it this time? If it's candy, give it to me. I'll give it to Lan."

"It's not candy. She took my last gift, you know. I'm learning."

Vinh kicks the dirt. "I still don't get it."

A nurse directs us to Ward B, and we climb urine-smelling stairs. We open a door to a second-floor room with twenty beds, some with two or three people in them. Annie's alone in a bed by a window, a clean bandage around her head. She already looks better. She sees us, turns her head away, and feigns sleep.

"I told you she wouldn't talk to us," Vinh whispers.

I drag him to the side of her bed, lean forward, and put the bag on the floor beside her. Then we retreat to the foot of her bed.

"Tell her it's for the others," I say.

Vinh clears his throat nervously and chokes out the words in formal Vietnamese.

Silence. She doesn't move. Then in a very low voice and without looking at us she says, "Thank you. Things are better for them now."

My heart races. My mind speeds up, too, trying to think of something intelligent to say.

"Ask her how long she's been a VC."

For the first time she glances at me, and then away as if she's studying both me and the question. "Five years."

Five years! I think. *She rose so high, was given so many positions in such a short time.*

"Ask her what she did before that and why she became a VC?"

Vinh looks anguished. "No, she'll say, 'you know' again."

"I think not. Do it."

Painfully, Vinh gets it out. She looks at both of us, and her answer goes to Vinh. "Everyone in my village was poor. A few rich people in Huế and Quảng Trị owned all the land. My mother and father died when I was young. My aunts raised me. I worked in the rice fields like everyone else. When I was eighteen, the police started taking me to District Headquarters. They thought I was already a VC. Sometimes they kept me there a few days."

My heart sinks. Did that start the abuse now written all over her? I try to lift my spirits and make another big mistake.

"Vinh, tell her the government has a program called 'Land to the Tiller.' If she tells us the names of the rich people who own all the land, we can work to get it redistributed to the people who have been working it for years."

Vinh gets it all out and a veil of suspicion drops over her face. "I don't know who the rich people are," she says. "I only heard stories. My head hurts. I can't talk anymore."

Vinh tugs me toward the door.

"Wait, just one more question. Ask her this. In Hải Lăng we saw her physical prowess and courage. In the PIK, she was there longer than anyone. How, where does she get the inner and outer strength to do all that?"

Vinh, looking at the end of his rope, says, "What does 'physical prowess' mean?"

"Skill and strength. She's got it. Plus courage."

"OK, OK," he says, his brow furrowed and shining with sweat. "I'll do it."

I watch her carefully while he translates. She listens intently, glances at me, and gives him the answer. "About Hải Lăng, I told you before. You were trying to kill me. I was trying to get away. About the Province Interrogation Center, I had nothing to give them. I'm no one, just a messenger, just a woman. That's all."

Vinh bolts for the door and I follow. At the door I turn to say, "Thank you, Miss," and catch her watching us. Heart pumping, I chase Vinh down the reeking stairs and across the dusty courtyard.

Vinh leans against the Scout's door. "I never want to talk to her again!"

"Why?" I smile. "She's charming."

"She's VC!" Vinh says, pulling out his Marlboros. "She'd kill us if she could."

"I thought you were quitting," I say, as he lights up.

"Tomorrow," he says. "When I don't have to talk to Miss Nữ."

On the way to the Chiêu Hội Center, I turn into the compound of the Special Police, and park near the office of their commander, Đại uý Rang, "Captain Tooth."

"Oh, no," Vinh groans. "Another scary place and more scary people."

"You don't have to get out. I'm just picking up something."

Vinh shivers. "Not from 'Captain Tooth,' I hope. He probably scares the VC into talking with his looks."

"Relax, think about Lan. I'll be right back."

Vinh gazes around at the squat, dark buildings of the compound. "Here, Hell," he says. "Lan, Heaven."

I walk to Rang's office. The CIA-advised Special Police are responsible for ferreting out, capturing, or killing, the VC infrastructure—like Annie. I don't like Rang. He's arrogant, mean, truly scary, and seems to like Americans about as much as he does the VC.

Rang's sergeant is not at the front desk, so I knock on the door. No answer. I knock again. What sounds like a growl comes from within. I take that as "enter" and open the door. Rang sits smoking behind a stack of dossiers. The top one reads, "Interrogation Report— Hoàng Thị Nữ."

Rang's face is asymmetrical, pock-marked, and twisted by injury, illness, or vocation into a diabolical mask. *Surely*, I think, *torturing other human beings as a business leaves its mark. And, I realize, that was Rang's jeep outside the PIK.*

"Mr. Chiêu Hội," Rang says sarcastically, "how many lies have you heard today from false ralliers? Send them to me if you want the truth."

"You said you would loan me Miss Nữ's Interrogation Report."

He picks it up and drops it in front of me. "It's nothing, she's nothing. Lowest kind of Commo-Liaison lackey. Stupid woman didn't even know the content of the messages she carried. I have to send this translation to our advisors in the Regional Center. Have it back by noon tomorrow. She's nothing but dust, filthy dust."

I walk out with the dossier under my arm. *She beat them,* I think. *She beat Giang and she beat Rang. And she talked to Vinh and me!*

We drive through town toward the Center. Quảng Trị is bustling with people going to and from the market. In front of the tailor shop, a crowd of excited people gather around something big stretched out on the ground.

"Oh my God," Vinh says. "A tiger!"

We get out and push into the crowd. The tiger is unbelievably huge, beautiful, magnificent, noble, and scary even in death. Around it, people talk in awestruck, hushed tones. The tailor stands in the doorway of his shop looking proud. Vinh pushes over to him. They talk, and Vinh brings back the word.

"Marines killed the tiger last night. They heard something and thought it was the VC sneaking up on their ambush position. The tailor is an old tiger hunter. The Marines brought it here for him to prepare the skin. They're going to take it back to the States."

We stare at it for a while in silence. *Another casualty of the war,* I think. *Even dead, it's the most magnificent animal I've ever seen.*

"It's beautiful," Vinh says. "If Lan was an animal, she'd be a tiger."

Back in the Scout, Vinh looks down at the dossier between us. "I still don't get why you're so interested in her?"

"Who's the most remarkable person you've ever met?"

"Lan, of course. I melt when I see her."

We bump along the bamboo-lined road to the Center.

"Okay, for me it's Miss Nữ. What I saw her do the night she was captured and what she's endured since put in her in a class

93

all by herself. To me, she's a superhero, like the kind I worshiped as a kid, and wanted to be like them."

Bamboo scrapes the sides of the Scout, and a woman with two heavy, sloshing buckets of water on the ends of her carrying pole steps aside as we pass.

"Superheroes worked for good," Vinh says.

"Who's to say who's good or bad?" I say.

Vinh snorts. "The VC are bad! How about those two old men killed in Cổ Luỹ? I'll tell you something else that's bad: Cổ Hồng on the Love Team. You know she sold herself to at least two Marines. They did it in the buffalo shed behind the church. One was the redhead Carter, who was chasing her around the straw stack acting like a gorilla. The people in the villages won't like it. She'll give the Love Team a bad reputation."

I feel my heart beating fast. That baby face, hip-length hair, and lush body, available for a few *đồng*?

"I'll talk to Chief Thuận about it."

Vinh is relentless. "Believe me, it will give us all a bad reputation. The VC will gain from it. They use things like this against you Americans. You know they do. Lan won't like me being around her either."

We turn into the Center, and I take Annie's dossier into my office. The Chief's out; I'll talk to him about Hồng later. I open the folder, and look up at the big wall map, the green mountains of the Ho Chi Minh Trail. *Annie lived out there, in the world of the tiger.*

I start to read, skimming down the pages of translated questions and answers, wincing with each one as I imagine the blows that accompanied them.

"Who helped you in the villages? Who hid you, gave you food?"

"I don't know their names. It was always dark. I couldn't see

94

their faces. We didn't talk."

After several pages of this and the repeated, "I'm no one, just a messenger, just a woman," I start to feel dizzy and sick. I shut up the folder in my desk drawer. I sit there feeling stunned. I had started to hear the blows, imagine the electric shocks, see her reeling, smell the stench of an evil, airless room.

From the APT barracks I hear drums, guitars, singing: Ky, Lam, and Vinh are rehearsing for the next Love Team show. I look up again at my map and think how I could help her escape from the hospital, go back to the wild and green world where she started her last mission.

In her condition now I don't think she could make it, I say to myself. *When she's stronger, maybe . . .*

I jump up, go out to my Scout, and call across the courtyard to Vinh, "I'm going to the PX, want anything?"

"Marlboros!" he shouts back. "One carton, not the soft pack. The flip-top box! Not for me, for Ky and Lam!"

Yeah, right, I think.

"And we're going on operation soon," Vinh shouts. "The Chief told them."

"Very good," I shout.

I drive to the PX and get more vitamins, insect repellent, oranges, and canned food. *What she can't use, she can trade,* I think. *I'll just put it by her bed — for the others.*

In the morning I toss the dossier in my Scout, put the PX bag beside it, and drive to the hospital. I run up the urine-smelling stairs with the bag, pass a nurse outside Ward B, and go in. The room is mostly empty. There's someone else in Annie's bed, sleeping or unconscious. My eyes search wildly around the room. *She's not here.*

I go out and ask the nurse, "Where are the people who were in this room?"

"*Cảnh sát*," she says. "Police came and took them away. I don't know where. They were VC."

I run down the stairs, drive to Rang's office, and go in with the dossier.

"Is the Captain in?" I ask the sergeant.

"Yes," he says, and he goes inside.

I hear voices. He comes out, holds the door open, and closes it behind me. It is not comfortable being in a closed room with Captain Tooth. I put the dossier on his desk. He leans back and looks at it.

"So, you saw nothing of interest."

"She's been moved. She's not in the hospital."

He sits up, throws the file aside, and snarls, "I move them all, the ones that could move. They were there with no guard, maybe escape. Some to Province Prison, some to Retraining Center. I sent her to Retraining Center. Maybe they make a good citizen out of her."

He laughs a chilling laugh and rocks back in his chair. "Why you so interested in her? She's nothing, know nothing, stupid."

I feel a dark force rise within me and a fear that I'm about to do something violent and dumb. I wisely catch myself on the violent part, but the dark force still comes out in words. "Our recent rallier, Xuân, says the VC in the mountains were 'very sad' when she was captured because she's important."

"*Bam!*" Rang slams his fist down on her dossier. "Lies!" he shouts. "Ralliers tell you anything, so I won't send them to prison. I know everything about her and she's nothing!"

I walk out, kicking myself. *Why did I say all that? Why did I let myself get drawn into his darkness? The consequences of this could be bad.* Then another voice says, *Get real. Stop beating up on yourself. He interrogates ralliers, too. It's not like you're telling him something he doesn't already know. Relax. Focus on helping her.*

I drive past the Province Prison to the adjacent Retraining Center, like the prison but not as bad, a place for the re-education of low-level VC and sympathizers. I get out with my PX bag, go in, and ask to see Miss Hoàng Thị Nữ.

"She's in the courtyard with the others. They're all on their break now."

I go through a barred door and into a courtyard crowded with miserable-looking people in rags, and some in dirty hospital gowns. Annie is among them in the bloodstained clothes she was captured in. She looks relapsed from the progress she made in Ward B, her mouth agape, her sunken eyes dark, and her skin a deathly pallor.

"Pass this bag to her," I say to those nearest me, and over their heads, I ask her, "What can I do for the others?"

"*Áo quần*," she says dully, as if each word is an effort. "Clothes. Many people have no clothes."

"I'll do what I can."

I drive to the house of my Mennonite friends, young pacifist teachers from Pennsylvania teaching English in the local high schools. Then I call my buddy, John Frechette of CARE in Đà Nẵng. They all agree to put together boxes of clothes.

The following day the Love Team goes out again, minus Cổ Hồng, and I go with them to Phường Láng Đồng Hamlet on the Street Without Joy and the upper end of the Lâm Thủy Forest. I go on night ambush with the APT while the Love Team does its show, and Võ Công Đỗ remains hidden and silent. We stay out three nights, all in Annie country. The people feed us dog—it's a Catholic, not Buddhist, hamlet—and welcome us into their homes to talk about Chiêu Hội. I'm eager to get back.

We return to the Center, and two big boxes of clothes are waiting for me in my office. I rush home, shower, shave, and drive to the Retraining Center. The warden sees me coming, lugging my two big boxes, and he meets me at the barred courtyard door. On the other side, ragged inmates crowd around.

"Clothes for them," I say. "But I'd like to deliver them to Miss Nữ. It was her request."

"She's not here," the warden says.

My heart sinks. "Where?"

"Special Police came and got her. Captain Rang's orders. They took her to the Regional Interrogation Center. She must be pretty important VC. We'll pass out your clothes."

I drag myself back to my Scout. *I did this to her,* I think. *I got drawn into Rang's darkness, and now I'm just as bad. I sent her to the Regional Interrogation Center, where the highest-ranking and hardest-core VC are broken. Now she's going through an even worse version of Hell, and I'm responsible, guilty again.*

Another voice answers: *Get off it. Rang's playing with you and her. He knows more than you about her, he just couldn't get it out himself. It's not your fault, it's not on you.*

Oh, yes, it is, the first voice says, as I drive heavily back to the Center, climbing in and out of the potholes with bamboo brushing the sides of my Scout, whispering, *"Guilty."*

I deserve to be shot, the first voice says.

I park in a cloud of dust by the flagpole and Chief Thuận's voice comes flying out of his office window. "Cố vấn, come inside. I have something amazing to tell you!"

He meets me on the top step and rushes me into his office. "Sit, I'll have to stand, I'm too agitated by this idea."

I sit at his desk and he looks out the door and up and down the corridor. "No one listening," he says. "This is hot." He pulls his chair around the desk and places it close to mine. Then he leans close and says, "It came to me in a dream last night."

I begin to be suspicious. He seems a little crazy.

"Listen–" He looks again to make sure no one's coming. "We

have a Love Team and it's doing great. Now we form, separate from the Love Team, and not part of its operations, a Night Ambush Team!"

I feel a surge of energy go through me.

"Look," he says, "we have Lúc-Thanh, Một, Bốn, Nam, more—they are the experts, the best. And they know the VC, the trails they use, their hideouts and supporters. We go with them, you and me. Vinh, too, if he wants to. And your friend Ramos. He can bring a radio and M-60. We're sure to meet the VC."

"Hmm," I say. "I doubt if Vinh—"

"No, what do you say? It's very important that you're in. You will have to coordinate and clear the places we operate with the Americans. We don't want to run into the Marines or the ARVN out there."

"No, no. Definitely not!"

"But are you in?"

"This is what I need. When do we start?"

"I knew you'd like it. I'll talk to Đặng Sỹ and Lúc-Thanh. We'll only take the APT we trust."

"Good plan."

Đặng Sỹ and Lúc-Thanh choose the twelve APT they trust the most and who had the most experience in night ambush with the VC. Vinh surprises me. He wants to go, once at least, and Chief Thuận, too, though I'll believe it when I see it.

The chosen APT go back to their home villages and troll for information. Một brings back something hot. Local VC from his home hamlet southeast of Quảng Trị City have been guiding NVA recon teams on missions that seem like preparations for the long-expected NVA assault on the city. Một believes if we go unseen into the dunes south of town and are in position before they start to move, we can ambush them.

"That's it!" Chief Thuận says. "That's our first mission. We go tonight. Cố vấn, your job is to clear it with the Americans. Make sure no units are operating there tonight without telling anyone *we'll* be there."

"Got it," I say, my heart pounding.

We all leave to prepare for night. I know how I can do this tricky maneuver of clearing an area without giving it away, but it will require a deal with my good ol' buddy, Puerto Rican Army Sergeant Eddie Ramos of the Mai Linh District Advisory Team. I know, too, what Ramos will require for his cooperation, and I want that too: his participation. I drive to Mai Linh on Quảng Trị's southern edge, where, as at Vinh's house, the city suddenly ends, and the countryside begins. Ramos is on radio watch, feet propped up, and reading a thick book by Ayn Rand. Like me, he's on his third year in Vietnam, volunteering to go back each time his one-year tour ends. Though he has a beautiful Puerto Rican wife back in New York City, he loves the Vietnamese people, land, culture, food, and *action*. To the hiss of his big PRC-25 radio, he swings his booted feet off the table, stands up, grins, and says, "OK, what you got?"

"It's big. I don't know if you're ready for this."

He pulls at the end of his Pancho Villa moustache and says in his husky, New York-Puerto Rican accent, "I'm ready, I'm over-ready. *Nada* going on around here for too long. Let's get some *action* going."

"I need to know there's no ops planned in a grid square north of Thương Xá Hamlet and the approach to it through the dunes from Highway One."

Ramos's dark eyes glow as he pulls his moustache. "I don't know, *hermano*. I didn't hear nothing about our usual deal. Am I in?"

"You're in, *claro que sí*, you're in. We need you."

"Now you're talkin'!" He goes to his big wall map of Mai

Linh District as it stretches south toward Hải Lăng. On it are plotted the U.S. and South Vietnamese operations for a twenty-four-hour period. We study it carefully, especially the dunes near Thương Xá, where the paddy-sea begins and rolls down the coast to Hải Lăng. *Annie's territory again,* I think. *I wonder if she knows Thương Xá, too?*

"All clear, *'mano,*" Ramos says. "Now what are we going to do there tonight?"

We sit down and I tell him. His eyes glow even more fiercely.

"*Perfecto!*" he says. "I'll bring the radio and an M-60. We could hit heavy shit, man, with the NVA out there."

"Come to the Center at 1700."

"I'll be there."

I go home and begin what becomes a ritual. Try to sleep and mostly toss and turn to the ticking of my clock and the hum of my air conditioner. Alarm goes off at 4:30 and I put on my record player Creedence Clearwater Revival's "Tombstone Shadow." I dress in Marine camo, jungle boots, and my lucky soft camo hat with slits for leaves. I keep playing "Tombstone Shadow" as I paint my face, hands, neck, wrists, even my eyelids black with camo paint. I strap on my pistol belt, .38 pistol and holster, and I take my new KAR-15, a shortened "jungle" version of the M-16, out of my closet, and snap a magazine loaded with eighteen rounds into it. I get out two more loaded mags and put them into separate pants pockets so they won't clink together, and I put a canteen, completely full so it won't gurgle, into my pack. I swallow a Dexamyl, a diet pill the MILPHAP doctors say will keep me awake all night, especially if I take another about midnight, and I put a handful into my shirt pocket for Ramos and the APT. While "Tombstone Shadow" still plays, I look at myself in the full-length mirror on my closet door and say, "Black Like Me," the title of a book I read in college about a white man who changes his skin color in order to discover what being black in America is like. I think about Annie, wonder what's happening to her, and if I'll live through the night. I turn off "Tombstone Shadow" and go out the door. My shadow follows me out to the Scout.

At the Center I park in the courtyard by the big ceremonial urn. Two ranks of twelve APT are drawn up by the flagpole with Lúc-Thanh standing in front of them. Đặng Sỹ is off to the side. He'll have charge of guarding the Center.

Chief Thuận comes out in tailored APT tiger-stripe, pistol belt, and M-16. Behind him is Vinh, amazingly clad in a Marine steel-pot helmet with camo cover, and a bulky Marine flak jacket, with an M-16 and a bandolier of ammunition.

"Looking good, Vinh," I say.

"The APT think I'm scared," Vinh says. "But I'm not. I just don't want to be in the army. Too much discipline."

Ramos pulls up in a jeep and unloads his radio and M-60 machine gun. APT crowd around, excited at the high-tech and extra firepower. Lúc-Thanh calls them back into formation and gives Ramos a big grin and thumbs-up.

Chief Thuận chooses two stay-behind APT to drive our vehicles out and back.

Lúc-Thanh says, "Not yet. Don't load. Wait." He points at the sky.

I know what he's waiting for, the narrow slit between day and night, which we'll slip through to our ambush positions, not too early to be seen and not too late for the VC to be already moving and maybe ambush us.

Ramos is on fire. "Let's go, 'mano, let's go," he says. "Let's get out there and do it. Đi!" he calls to Lúc-Thanh. "Go!"

"Chưa!" Not yet! Lúc-Thanh shouts back.

Finally, just when Ramos is about to jump out of his skin, Lúc-

Thanh says the magic word, "*Đi!*" Go!

We jam into the APT pickup and my Scout, bump and jostle out the gate, past the Citadel, and flying down Highway One. No traffic now. It's already too late for anyone to be driving the roads outside the city limits. This is VC time, when "Indian Country" becomes the night, as well as the forest and mountains. Annie's time.

Where the dunes roll close to the highway, Một signals a stop. We pile out fast and the return drivers take over, eager to get back to town but not eager, I hope, to spread the word about us.

Một takes the lead, and we fall in at five-meter intervals and begin wending our way through the dunes, staying to low places as the big shadow from the mountains crawls over the land.

Ramos, carrying the radio and the M-60, and itching to get into position, moves up behind Một and me. Suddenly, around a curve in the rolling dunes, Một drops onto the sand like a stone, and comes crawling to us backwards.

"ARVN ahead!" Một gasps. "Setting up a machine gun."

We peer around the base of the dune and see three Regional Force soldiers setting up an M-60 to fire right down our lane.

"Shit!" Ramos whispers. "They're s'posed to be two clicks to the south!"

"We gotta show ourselves before they see the APT," I whisper.

"Let's do it," he whispers.

We stand and walk around the dune saying in English first and then Vietnamese, "Americans! Don't shoot! There's more people coming."

The RF look up in surprise as they see the APT behind us in a variety of uniforms, and many with VC weapons. Beyond the three are more RF getting into ambush positions. Ramos and I wave, making sure they see us, and they go back to getting comfortable and digging in.

"Damn!" Ramos whispers. "A little later and a little darker and we might have walked right into that '60."

Who else is out of position? I wonder, as the night bears down on us and Một quickens his pace on a swing to the south.

Soon we'll be in Hải Lăng, I think. *Annie's territory.* But then Một swings back to the north, climbs halfway up a big dune, lies down, and peers over the edge. Ramos and I crawl up, lie beside him, and look over, too, and behind us the rest go down and stay still. Below, where the dunes meet the paddies, the thatched houses of Thương Xá Hamlet rise as if grown on the land, and the last lights — candles and lanterns — wink out as the darkness of true night rolls over us all.

Lúc-Thanh pulls us back to the main body behind the big dune and he and Một begin putting us into ambush positions and pointing out our fields of fire. First, Ramos with the M-60, Vinh and the Chief with their '16s, and me, covering a space between two dunes that leads down to Thương Xá. After telling us with gestures where to focus, and where not to shoot, they vanish into black to emplace the rest. Ramos lies to my right, then the Chief, and barely visible, just a dark bump on the sand, Vinh in his helmet and flak jacket.

I lie staring, eyes boring into the empty space I'm supposed to cover, and misgivings begin to fill my mind. Lúc-Thanh and Một have put all the non-ex-VC into the same position. We could easily all be taken out by a couple of grenades or a burst of automatic fire by anyone in the positions now invisible to us. I twist and look in the direction Lúc-Thanh and Một disappeared. Nothing. No one, just black night and rolling dunes. Six feet away, Ramos snuggles behind his gun, itching, I know, to let it rip down into the valley below us. Six feet from him, Chief Thuận seems restless and is making soft, stirring noises. I start wishing I hadn't given him the Dexamyl and that he'll soon fall asleep.

Beyond him, Vinh stirs, too, no doubt hot and uncomfortable in the steel pot, and with the steel plates of the flak jacket between him and the soft earth. Mosquitoes sing in my ears, and I stare at my space thinking, *Why did Một put us all here? We should have been spread out among the other teams. Is he a VC? Lúc-Thanh? All of them? But no, they all worked together to capture Annie. And what can be happening to her now?*

I try to banish her from my mind along with the thought that I deserve whatever's going to happen to me out here.

Suddenly the night explodes. From the dunes to our left, long, ripping bursts stream down into the valley. Then Vinh starts shooting, at what I can't see. The Chief begins crawling rapidly backwards, saying in terror, "Many VC! Many VC!" Ramos, fierce behind his gun, shouts, "Where are they? Where are they?" and he begins firing short, repeated bursts of the fast-shooting M-60. Then bullets come streaming and cracking over our heads from our left rear and Ramos starts to turn the gun around till another burst lower overhead sends us plunging our faces down in the sand. We're being attacked from the rear!

Another long burst rips downslope from the left, where the firing started, and a cry of pain comes up.

"*Có một người!* We got one!" a shout bursts from the left.

Ramos talks low and fast on the radio and the 105s at Mai Linh start firing illumination rounds. In their light and among the giant dancing shadows of dunes and bushes, we see APT on our left moving cautiously down, weapons at hip-level and ready to shoot. Ramos picks up the '60 and heads down, too, and Vinh and I follow.

"Here!" an APT shouts.

We rush to a form in a brown uniform, writhing, moaning, and bleeding on the ground from a bullet hole just below his knee. Ramos and Bốn whip out field dressings and tightly bind his wound.

"Northerners!" he moans. "They ran away and left me! Northerners!"

"I know him," Một says. "It's Sướng. He's from Thương Xá. He's been guiding the NVA recon teams. He's a long-time VC."

"He's going to die," Lúc-Thanh says, "if we don't get him to a hospital. We can't stop that bleeding. Cố vấn, tell Sergeant Ramos to call for a truck to meet us on the highway five kilometers down Highway One. We'll carry him there."

Ramos gets on the radio as the last flare burns out.

Surprisingly, the Mai Linh District Chief agrees. He'll send a truck for all of us five kilometers past the city limits.

Again, I'm in awe of Lúc-Thanh and the APT. They're going to make a dangerous night march through the dunes and then take an equally hazardous ride on a road no one drives after dark to save the life of an enemy. Then a voice in my head says, *Or is he their enemy?*

The APT rig up a sling from two shirts tied together, load him in it, and with Một leading, we take a circling route through the dunes back toward the road.

Ramos comes up behind me and whispers, "*Amigo*, those rounds that went over our heads were fired from one of our own positions."

"I know," I whisper back over my shoulder as my boots sink into the sand.

"Somebody on our team was tryin' to take us out, man."

"I know. I'm gonna talk to Đặng Sỹ and Lúc-Thanh about it. I want to find out who was in the position just to the left of us."

"There it is, '*mano*."

We crouch by the edge of the road with Sướng, the VC, moaning on the ground. A big 2-½ ton truck from the District comes roaring down the road loaded with Regional Forces soldiers. We load Sướng in, squeeze in ourselves, and rumble back to the sleeping city.

In the province hospital's emergency room, a male nurse sits dozing by the door. The APT put Sướng on a table. The nurse doesn't move. I go and stand over him, black-painted and armed.

"You going to take care of him?" I say in Vietnamese.

He looks at Sướng and then me. "Yeah," he says. He still doesn't move.

"We did what we could," Ramos says, as we go out the door. "We got him here."

We climb back aboard the truck and it rumbles down empty, dark streets to the Chiêu Hội Center. We're all still flying on adrenaline and Dexamyl.

I go home, put on "Tombstone Shadow," and begin what becomes my post-op ritual, hanging up my lucky hat, stashing my weapons in the back of my closet, dancing to the music as I strip off my camo shirt and pants in front of my full-length mirror, my face black-smeared from sweat and paint. Suddenly I'm rocked by *another* face looking back at me, an Indian in war paint and feathers doing a war dance and staring into my eyes. I plop down on my bed as if pushed, and sit upright looking into the mirror, where the Indian is still dancing and staring at me. The vision passes and I see myself again.

For a moment I'm elevated. *I saw myself in another life! Reincarnation is real. I've felt since kid-times I was an Indian. My first memory of seeing myself in a mirror was that I looked all wrong, I was supposed to have brown eyes, not blue, and black hair with feathers, and copper-colored skin. This proves it. I was an Indian!*

Elation quickly turns to gloom. *But wait,* I think. *If reincarnation is about learning from life to life, here I am still war-painted and doing the war dance. I haven't learned. I haven't progressed. I'm still doing as I did in my last warrior life.*

I go in my shower and wash off the black paint. "Tombstone Shadow" plays to the end. I lie down thinking about Annie.

The next morning I drive to the hospital to check on Sướng as I had once driven to see Annie. *Was she still in the Regional Interrogation Center? Was she still alive?*

"The VC?" a nurse says in the ER. "He's in Ward B. You know where it is?"

"I know," I say.

I climb the same urine-smelling stairs. Sướng is asleep or unconscious, lying on his back, and covered with a sheet up to his chin. There's a terrible emptiness all along his lower right side.

A nurse across the room is at the side of a bed with two people in it.

"This man, how is he?" I call.

"The VC?" she says. "They cut off his leg."

I feel hit by a hammer in the stomach.

"Cut where?" I say, looking at the flattened sheet.

She stands where I can see her and draws a line with her finger from high on her thigh around to her hip.

I feel sick. *They cut off his whole leg. He was wounded below the knee!*

"I'm not the doctor," the nurse says as she turns away.

Back at the Center, Lúc-Thanh comes into my office and places a small, brown-colored metal object in my hand. On it are the words in Vietnamese, "Determined to Fight, Determined to Win," another slogan of Hồ Chí Minh.

"Sướng's medal," Lúc-Thanh says. "He was a good VC. We want you to have it."

And now he has one leg, I think. I close my hand around it, drop it into my pocket, and feel its sharp point against my thigh.

I lose myself in the war, out two days and nights a week with the Love Team, two or three nights with the Ambush Team. Vinh continues performing with the Love Team. The Chief stays back. Ramos goes when he can. The Ambush Team soon attains the highest contact rate in the province. Almost every night we're involved in some kind of action. A few false ralliers reveal themselves and are dealt with by the APT. I try not to think too much about Annie as I paint my face black and listen to "Tombstone Shadow." The Indian doesn't reappear. He's made his point.

Suớng is released from the hospital, interrogated by Rang, given crutches by the MILPHAP Team, and sent to prison. Vinh and I visit him there. He says he'll take us to his old bunker in the dunes where there are probably weapons and possibly the NVA recon team that deserted him when he was wounded.

Lúc-Thanh puts together a rare daytime operation, the elite of the Ambush Team, Ramos, and me. At dawn the APT pickup drops us off on Highway One where a line of ironwood trees meets the dunes. With Ramos carrying Suớng on his back, we weave through the trees and are soon lost to sight from the road. With Suớng guiding from atop Ramos's back, we wind and trudge our way through the dunes, keeping always to the low passes and valleys connecting them. The sun begins to hammer us, except for Suớng, who's in shorts and his loose VC shirt. We're all soaked in sweat. Ramos, who's in great shape and prides himself on being *fuerte como un toro*," "strong as a bull," begins to stagger, and Nam, tallest of the APT, takes over.

We go deeper into the dunes and closer to Thương Xá. When Nam begins to falter, I take Suớng. Nam and Ramos lift him onto my back, a painful move for him, and I wrap my left arm under his remaining leg and my right arm under his still-tender stump. He indicates the direction, and we go on trudging through the sand.

Even with one leg missing, he's heavy, and now I'm sinking deeper into the sand with each step. His body heat is also now added to mine, his breath on my neck, his chest and stomach under his thin shirt all down my sweat-soaked back, and worst of all, his balls inside his thin shorts, swaying and bumping with each step against the base of my spine.

I begin to think of my responsibility for this. If I hadn't been so enthusiastic about the Chief's idea of a Night Ambush Team, if I had refused to believe we could safely clear an area to operate in. . . . Sweat runs into my eyes. Sướng's balls bump against my spine. I sweat and trudge on and try to shut out the feeling.

Just when I'm about to call for relief, Sướng says, "There, the secret bunker is there."

We look where he's pointing. Through my sweat-glazed eyes all I see are blazing dunes and a low dike at the beginning of the paddy-sea, dry and fallow now in the heat of summer.

Nam and Lúc-Thanh help Sướng off my back and Một, who's been carrying his crutches, puts them under his armpits. Sướng steadies himself and talks excitedly to the APT, too fast for me and Ramos to follow.

Lúc-Thanh turns to us. "Cố vấn, you and the sergeant stay here. The bunker is just past the corner of the dike. We'll check it out. Don't move from this place. There may be booby traps."

Ramos and I lie down with our weapons trained on the corner of the dike. The APT move forward with Sướng hobbling on his crutches. When they reach the dike, they spread out in a semi-circle. Sướng and Lúc-Thanh carefully approach the corner and Sướng points out what looks like just another tuft of grass growing at the dike's edge. Lúc-Thanh reaches down, his hands disappear in the sand and then he suddenly jerks upward in an explosion of sand and dry tufts of grass. The wooden cover of an underground bunker comes flying up, revealing a dark tunnel entrance.

Lúc-Thanh throws the wooden cover aside, drops to the ground and lies aiming his AK-47 at the black hole of the tunnel opening. Sướng stays standing, swaying on his crutches, and peering into the hole.

"*Không có người*," he says to Lúc-Thanh. "No people."

The APT gather around the hole. Một, smallest of them, crawls inside. Sướng says something and the APT back away from the hole.

"I hope to hell there's no booby traps in there," Ramos rasps in his husky voice. "That Một is a brave little dude."

Một comes out, his elfin face shining.

"*Không có gì*," he says. "Nothing in there."

Sướng looks crestfallen, "*Không có AK*? There's no AK?"

"*Không có gì hết*," Một says. "There's nothing at all."

"I'm sorry," Sướng says to the APT. "I can show you another one. It's not too far."

"No," Lúc-Thanh says. "We go back."

I take my turn carrying Sướng back to the highway. Again, there's the terrible bump-bump-bump, and the feeling of responsibility. *Does he have children? Will he have children?*

The next morning is Sunday. I stay at home writing letters to my mom and sisters back in Iowa, and to my *hanai* (adopted) mother in Hawaii. I don't write anything about Annie or Sướng. I keep it light, tell them about the Love Team, Vinh and Lan, Ramos and the Chief, hopes for peace.

"*Cố vấn!*" a familiar voice calls at my door. It's Việt!

"*Vào đi!*" I call back. "Come in!"

Việt, my ex-VC friend, and guide on seven operations on the Ho Chi Minh Trail, is now working as a Kit Carson Scout for the "Grim Reaper" recon teams of the U.S. 1st Brigade of the 5th Mechanized Division. Việt, the amazing "*thổ công*" or "earth god," the Vietnamese term for those completely skilled and immersed in nature. I had saved Việt (his VC name) from being put into prison after he was captured by Rang. And Việt had saved me several times on the Ho Chi Minh Trail.

Việt comes bursting into my small room, filling it with his usual high energy. "*Cố vấn, lâu ngày quá! It's a long time! Too long!*"

Việt and I have a great almost-family relationship. The APT even call him "Cố vấn's son." Betrayed for money as Annie was, Việt was captured by Rang, brutally beaten, and given a choice — cooperate or die. Rang then "loaned" him to me because Việt knew the mountain and forest world of the Ho Chi Minh Trail and Rang did not have the assets to go out there, and I did, through first the Marines and when they withdrew, the Army's 5th Mech. Finally, Rang made Việt a deal he thought he would never have to pay off on. He would make Việt a rallier rather than a prisoner if Việt brought him a 122 mm. NVA rocket from our operations on the Trail. Việt did it after leading a night raid on an NVA Rocket Company's camp deep in the forest. Việt was truly a magic man in the wilds, growing up out there, and learning from the Bru tribal Montagnards. And even though he was only nineteen, he had been a VC since fifteen and had many times guided NVA units down the Ho Chi Minh Trail. I could understand his Vietnamese better than anyone's, and in return he always seemed to understand mine. Though he claimed to know no English, he had a favorite song.

"Cố vấn, put on my song," he says. "I haven't heard it since I was here last. It will cover what I'm going to tell you, too, just in case the guards or your maid are listening outside."

My heart speeds up. "You've got something hot?"

He lowers his voice. "Wait till you hear. Put on my song."

We had been through a lot and I mostly trusted Việt, but I

always buckled my seat belt while riding beside him in an open-door chopper. It also was somewhat troubling that he liked this particular song with its words about, as I understood it, treachery. I pull out my album of the Beatles' *Abbey Road* and put the needle down on "Maxwell's Silver Hammer."

"Ahhh," Việt says as he leans back in my one chair. "I love this song. Let me listen a minute; then I'll tell you the hot news."

I sit on the end of my bed and Việt closes his eyes as the Beatles sing, "Bang-bang, Maxwell's silver hammer came down on his head/ Bang-bang Maxwell's silver hammer made sure he was dead. . ."

"Keep playing it till it ends," Việt says. "Now I'll tell you. You know Nhân Biểu Hamlet across the river from Quảng Trị City and just before the Americans' Quảng Trị Combat Base? The VC are going in there three and four nights a week. They cross the old French railroad tracks south of the base, then into the hamlet to collect rice, recruit, and spread their message. We can ambush them! Use the APT Night Ambush Team and the Grim Reapers."

Alarm bells go off in my mind as the Beatles sing on. One grain of doubt I still have about Việt is that he keeps feeding me information and building on successes to rise to a larger and larger kill. The APT Ambush Team has been hurting the VC, and the Grim Reapers 5th Mech. Recon Teams have been finding parts of the Ho Chi Minh Trail. *Is this a plan to wipe both out? And me, too? "Bang-bang Maxwell's silver hammer came down on his head/ Bang-bang Maxwell's silver hammer made sure he was dead, oh-oh..."*

"Việt, how did you get this information?"

He lowers his voice and leans toward me. "My old contacts in the hamlet. I won't tell their names."

"Why would they help you? They must know you're on our side now."

"Their only son was taken by the local VC one year ago. They haven't heard from him since. They're afraid he's dead. And these same VC keep demanding more rice and sweet potatoes. This farmer and his wife have almost nothing to sell at the market and not that much to eat. They hate the VC now."

"OK, why do you want to do this? You work for the Grim Reapers now."

He leans back in his chair. Like Cổ Hồng, he has a plump, baby face, which is amazing considering all he's been through. "Cố vấn, I'm bored. The Grim Reapers are doing nothing these days. They only talk about going home. We fly in choppers out to the mountains, sit on a hilltop till we eat all our food. Then we fly back. We never see the VC. I'm afraid Captain Rang will find out I'm doing nothing, and he'll send me to prison."

"You got him the rocket."

Việt snorts. "You trust him? I don't. He's mean. He likes to hurt people."

"How do you want to do this?"

"Mixed team. Best of the APT, best of the Grim Reapers. Twelve people, four positions. Meet at sunset in the ditch outside the base's front gate. I'll lead to the railroad tracks and put the teams into position. Sometimes the VC go over the tracks, sometimes through a tunnel where a stream flows under a bridge. One man watches from the tracks for a light signal from the hamlet. When they see that, they all cross. Maybe twelve in all. They cross the paddy, go into the hamlet, and then break into teams of three. We'll hit them when they cross the tracks and get them all."

"Maxwell's Silver Hammer" ends. I start to play it again but Việt stands and says, "I have to go. You arrange for tomorrow night. I'll come back in the morning and you tell me."

"You've got it all figured out."

Việt smiles like I've seen him do before our other operations. "Now we just have to do it," he says.

He leaves and I hear his motor-scooter start outside and zoom away into the distance. His energy still vibrates in the room. *Who is Việt?* I think. *Is he simply a survivor and chameleon-like to stay alive, or a deeply embedded double agent building toward a big kill that will include me? Is there a connection with Annie here? Annie is captured, and Việt shows up with a plan.*

Abbey Road plays to the end as I think about Việt. I put my letter-writing aside and go out the door to my Scout. While waiting for old Huynh to drag open the gate, I stare across the street at the *Nhà xác*, the "Death House," where recently-killed South Vietnamese soldiers are brought to be claimed by their families. An empty ARVN truck sits ominously outside, and now, as my gate screeches and gouges the street, a Tri-Lambretta pulls up beside the truck and three young widows in white spill out and rush into the Death House. Immediately comes an explosion of screaming, crying, and unintelligible words. The screaming pursues me as I drive away, the hot wind chasing dry leaves to the side of the road.

Lúc-Thanh comes to my office, and he goes for Việt's plan right away. He'll put together a team of the best APT: Một, Nam, Luân, Bốn and him. With me it makes the six Việt wanted.

He grins, his bad eye rolling. "I think I know who shot at you in the dunes: Thu, the young guerrilla from Cam Lộ. He's off the Ambush Team, and I've got my eye on him."

Thu! I think. Friendly Thu. Too friendly.

"Very good." I say.

I drive along the river road with my mind churning. Essential now for Việt's plan to happen is the cooperation of the 5th Mech, not an easy thing to get with a giant, complex unit, especially under the new U.S. policy of "Vietnamization" of the war, and an emphasis on low or no American casualties. I cross the big bridge north of town, pass through the target hamlet of Nhân Biều, and enter the barbed and razor wire rings and heavily guarded main gate of Quảng Trị Combat Base. As the MPs wave me through, I see a rare sight, a bird (birds being among the major casualties of the war), a dove, sitting on a roll of dusty razor wire. *I hope that's a good omen,* I think, and I say a quick prayer for peace with a twinge of guilt about being on a war mission, still on the war path. *What does the Indian think of me now?*

I drive through the massive base toward the Brigade Headquarters. The base to me is a nightmare of Industrial Age civilization, a total contrast to the agricultural world outside. Where once were rice paddies, thatched houses, graves, shrines, temples, and birds, there are now motor pools, garbage dumps, chow halls, barracks, stinking latrines, poison-sprayed earth, minefields, watch-towers, and rolls of razor wire. And some very good guys, whose help and cooperation I need.

First on the list, Major "Bad Jose," the Brigade Intelligence Officer. Big, barrel-chested, black, and dynamic, he's both loved and feared by his underlings, who nicknamed him "Bad Jose" after a character in a popular song by Jay and the Americans. He sits at his desk gazing at a topographic map of the province with another enlarged map on the wall behind him with "Probable Locations of Enemy Units" plotted with little red-star flags. He and I became friends in the months of our operations with Việt on the Ho Chi Minh Trail.

"Mister Chiêu Hội," he says, looking up and grinning. "My favorite civilian—and the only one I know around here. To what do I owe the honor of this visit? You know we're deep in Vietnamization." He draws a line on the map with his finger around the base and spreads his big hands. "We're staying close to home and keeping our asses covered, and the word for that comes from the highest levels—like the President of the USA."

"Don't worry," I say. "This is *very* close to home and it's

Vietnamization at its best, combined forces, with the Vietnamese playing the leading role."

Bad Jose stands and smiles, "I *might* be able to sell this to the General, but he still remembers you dressing the ARVN Intel Team in NVA gear against his orders. Let's hear the rest."[1]

I tell him Việt's plan. He likes it. Standing, he reminds me of Sgt. Jones, who first treated Annie. Suddenly, for just an instant, I'm back in Hải Lăng with Jones holding the silver surgical scissors over his head and then under the bare bulb the blood from her ear spurting.

"Here's what we'll do," Bad Jose says. "Hey, did I lose you?"

"No, I was just—remembering something."

"We'll drive over to 1/11 and meet with their S-3, Ranger Joe Lukitsch. We'll get his OK for a Grim Reaper Team, fly an aerial recon in the 1/11 chopper, and then I'll sell it to the General, while you wait in the distance."

"Sounds good, except for the aerial recon. I don't want to tip off the VC."

"Choppers fly those railroad tracks numerous times every day. We'll make just one pass. I need to see this before I talk to the General. He'll expect it."

"OK, let's go."

We drive across the base to the Command Post of the 1st Battalion, 11th Infantry Regiment, the "Pioneers," a history-laden unit going back to the Indian Wars. Major "Ranger Joe" Lukitsch, fair-skinned and burly, the S-3 Operations Officer, is in the Ops Center, talking on the radio to one of his Grim Reaper recon teams. Starved for action under Vietnamization, he quickly arranges a chopper for us, and we troop out to steel-mesh Pioneer Pad, where a Huếy sits warming up on a painted image

1   This story told in my book *Mission on the Ho Chi Minh Trail*.

of a coonskin-cap-wearing frontiersman. Ranger Joe shouts to the pilot and away we go in a crescendo of engine power and whipping blades, no doors, blasting wind, tail up, nose down, and airborne. We're all grinning like fools, like kids on a carnival ride.

"Damn, I love this!" Ranger Joe shouts.

The pilot swings east over the industrial beehive of the base, then the river, and circling back west over the northwest edge of Quảng Trị City, the bridge with a truck convoy crossing, Nhân Biểu Hamlet and its maze of paths, gardens, thatched houses, banana groves, and manioc patches, and the old French Saigon-Hanoi Railroad Line, long ago blown up by the VC, the tunnel and stream under the tracks, fallow rice paddies, a graveyard with low, grass-grown mounds, scattered water buffalo grazing, the rings of wire protecting the base, squat sandbag bunkers, spindly watchtowers, and back again over Pioneer Pad.

"Did you get what you wanted, sir?" the pilot shouts back at Bad Jose.

"Got it!" he shouts, and then to us, "Now for the General."

We settle down on the vibrating steel mesh of the pad and Bad Jose takes off in his jeep while Ranger Joe and I descend into the 1/11 Tactical Operations Center, a huge "igloo" bunker of hundreds of sandbags and interspersed steel girders, to discuss Việt's plan. We'll meet at 1730 in the ditch outside the base's main gate. Ranger Joe will choose six of the top Grim Reapers. He'll also alert Base Security that a mixed team will be operating not far outside the wire tonight, and he'll clear it with Triệu Phong District Advisory Team to make sure RF and PF forces stay well away from the base perimeter.

"This is the part that scares me most," I say to Ranger Joe as we sip ice-cold Cokes from the TOC fridge. "Will everyone in those perimeter bunkers and watchtowers get the word? We're going to be in view as we start the move to our ambush positions and some of the APT will have VC weapons."

"I hear you," Ranger Joe says. "I will personally make sure that every troop in every position on that side of the base gets the word."

"I appreciate that."

"Damn, I wish I could go with you. The General would shit a brick if I did."

Bad Jose's jeep pulls up outside and he comes ducking through the sandbag tunnel leading into the TOC, filling it with his bulk. "We're on!" he says. "The General said yes, but" – he looks at me – "he said to remind you that he'll tolerate no more 'Batman Capers' in his Brigade."

Ranger Joe chokes on his Coke. "He can't forget about the ARVN on the Trail in NVA gear."

"Good thing I'm a civilian," I say.

"Hey, toss me a Coke," Bad Jose says. "And tell me what you've planned."

I drive slowly back to Quảng Trị City looking at the ditch we'll hide in, the rice paddy we'll walk through way too close to the base perimeter, the small stream we'll cross, the cemetery of grazed grave-mounds, the tunnel under the blown-up tracks, and the railroad embankment the VC will cross or come through. I see bushes and a few trees, probably the places Việt will put us for our ambush positions. I enter Nhân Biểu Hamlet and pull off to the side as a U.S. truck convoy rumbles across the one-lane bridge, and kids run out to the roadside shouting, "You gimme Sa-lem! You gimme can-dy! You gimme chop-chop!"

From the windows of the trucks and from soldiers riding on the mountains of supplies piled in the beds, G.I.s throw down a rain of C-ration cigarettes, candy, and food, and the kids run back to their houses with their treasures. *And several nights a week,*

I think, *the VC come to their homes. Tomorrow night we're going to meet them. I wish it was tonight.*

The convoy passes and I drive across the trembling bridge. Below, the broad Thạch Hãn River flows, down from the mountains and on to the sea. *Where is all this going?* I wonder. *Is Việt leading us into an ambush? Will Bad Jose and Ranger Joe be able to inform all the perimeter security about us being outside the wire? And is there a connection with Annie's capture?*

Driving down the dirt road to the Center, I hear a shout from outside a small, bamboo-shrouded house: "Cố vấn!"

A young, pretty woman in *áo dài* comes running out carrying a small boy in her arms. I stop and she approaches my window, her face flushed with excitement. The boy, maybe three years old, looks confused and a little scared.

"Cố vấn, you remember me?" she says in Vietnamese. "Biến's wife. This is his son."

A rush of memory and emotion overwhelms me, as I see the boy looks exactly like Biến, *brilliant* Biến, my best Vietnamese friend in Huế when I was the Refugee Advisor there in '66 and '67. Biến, who worked for USAID, and went on to be an interpreter for Bill McWhirter of *TIME Magazine*. Biến was taken from his house (and wife and child) by the VC in Tết '68 and murdered along with hundreds of others with Saigon-government and U.S.-ties in the dunes east of Huế. Through my tears I look at the boy's face and I choke out the words, "He looks just like his father."

"Yes," she says. "Everyone sees it. It's like Biến is here in him. My mother lives in that house. We're visiting from Huế and I saw you coming. You must come and eat with us."

"In two days I'll be free," I say. "Yes, that will be wonderful."

"See, son?" she says. "This was daddy's good friend." Then to me, "We call him little Biến."

I drive on with tears on my cheeks and my mind flooded with memories of Biến and Tom Gompertz of USAID, who was also killed in Huế in Tết '68, and Staff Sgt. "Goat" Hogan, killed south of Huế in '67, and Dwight Owen, killed in Quảng Ngãi Province in '66, four of my best friends in Vietnam gone. *Now is it my turn? Got to think about life. Biến's son: his face is just like his dad's. It's like Biến has come alive again in him. And his wife is as beautiful as ever. Life, got to think about life.*

I turn into the Center and see Lúc-Thanh heading for the APT barracks, where the sound of the Love Team girls singing is flowing out.

"*Tomorrow,*" I say to Lúc-Thanh. "We're going."

He grins and his bad eye rolls. "The Americans are in?"

"They're in. I'll pick you up here at 5."

"I wish it was tonight," he says. "Too many chances for leaks."

"That's the way Việt wanted it. And the Americans need time to prepare."

Lúc-Thanh fixes me with his good eye and I have a flash of how Annie pinned Vinh to the wall with her look.

"You trust Việt?" he says.

I shrug my shoulders and look off to the west. "He took us to the mountains and back seven times."[2]

"That's something," Lúc-Thanh agrees. "But Thu went on operation many times before he tried to kill you, the Chief, Ramos, and Vinh." He points to his good eye. "I've got my eye on Brother Việt."

"Good," I say. "Me, too."

I climb the headquarters steps and see Chief Thuận in his office, staring at a paper on his desk with his head in his hands.

"Come in, cố vấn," he says. "I've just received a shock. Look

---

2   These stories are in *Mission on the Ho Chi Minh Trail.*

at this."

He hands me a note written in Vietnamese, hastily scrawled, it looks to me. It's addressed to the Chief and signed by Phi, the ex-NVA rallier whom the Chief, surprisingly to the rest of us, since ex-NVA were generally regarded with suspicion, made his driver and valet, was often a guest at his home, drove the Chief's wife to the market, his kids to school, and earned the nickname among the APT of "the Chief's Little Brother."

It's filled with words unknown to me, though I do see "wife, children," and "eat rice." I hand it back. "Sorry, Chief, I can't read much Vietnamese."

"I'll translate." In a heavy voice he reads, "Dear Chief Thuận, I hope this finds you well. Your friendship and generosity to me have created a lasting bond and a brotherly love that will never be forgotten. I have a confession to make. My affection for you and your family was not, in the beginning, sincere. Now, on the eve of my departure, I must tell you: It was my mission to 'rally,' to enter the Chiêu Hội program to collect information on APT operations, to gain your confidence, and then, and this is the most heart-rending part of my confession, to kill you. You invited me into your home. I met your wonderful wife and children. We had meals together. We talked of many things and became like brothers. I often agonized over the final part of my mission and although I will have to answer for this, I realized that as a human being, I could not do it. As an officer in the glorious Army of our country and in the service of our beloved Uncle Hồ, I will continue to fight and work for success, 'Determined to Fight and Determined to Win,' but not at the loss of my humanity. I thank you for showing me that and wish you a long life and happiness. I hope we will meet again someday in peace. Your Brother, Phi."

The Chief looks up at me with tears in his eyes. "I won't tell my wife about this. I'll just tell her that he's gone."

I drive to my compound and go in my room. I feel like being alone. I sit in my chair and put my feet up on the bed. I think about my life. *I live in a world of deception, where things are almost always not what they seem. How much a part of this am I? Tomorrow night, for example, I'll be eagerly following the war path and hoping the VC will come to my position, but if I were Vietnamese, I'd probably be a VC. In three years in Vietnam, I've learned how corrupt the Saigon government is and how disastrous the U.S. presence has been for the Vietnamese people, land, and culture. Surely, I'd be one of Annie's men, ready to follow her anywhere, do anything under the slogan of "Nothing is more precious than independence and freedom," and wasn't that the battle cry of our revolution? And yet Annie was betrayed by one of her own men, her bodyguard. I live in a world of deception. One thing in all this seems real: Annie ran and swam through a storm of bullets, and she continues to resist the worst forms of torture, not giving up even one of her comrades. Could I follow her there? I have my doubts —*

"Cố vấn!"

That familiar kid-voice at my door! "Come in, Việt!"

Việt comes in dressed in Marine camo, looking chubby, his broad face glistening with sweat. "I can't stay. I saw you were home and thought I'd check. Are the Americans in?"

Immediately, I'm caught up in his enthusiasm. "They're in. The APT, too. Come here at 5 tomorrow. We'll pick up the APT and then go to the base."

"I'll come a little early. You have to play me my song before we go. We're going to meet the VC, cố vấn. That means we have to do everything right. Tell the APT and the Americans. I'll be walking point and they have to follow my plan completely. And you walk second, like always."

I feel my heart pounding, imagining us out there, moving through the night. "Like always," I say.

"OK, I got to go. See you tomorrow."

"Tomorrow."

He goes out and his Vespa speeds away. *Oh, Việt,* I think. *Who are you, really? Suddenly it strikes me: Annie may be the only person I know who is exactly who she seems to be. And what price can she be paying for it now?*

At 5 the next day, just as I finish dressing, arming, and painting up to "Tombstone Shadow," Việt arrives to listen to "Maxwell's Silver Hammer" and paint his face too. We drive to the Center, bumping down the bamboo-lined road. As we pass Biến's mother-in-law's house, Biến's wife and son come to the open door smiling and waving. When she sees us black-faced, her smile fades, and I imagine her reliving the night when the VC took Biến away.

"Who's that?" Việt asks.

"Wife of an old friend. I'll tell you later."

We turn into the Center. Lúc-Thanh, Nam, Một, Bốn, and Luân are sitting on the steps by the ceremonial urn.

"*Đi,*" I say. "Let's go."

Lúc-Thanh looks up at the sky. "Too early," he says. "Too much light, wait."

Việt leans across me and says out the window, "Go now. The Americans will be slow. I know. And we may have to wait on the bridge."

"*Đi,*" I say again.

They climb aboard and we drive the river road to the bridge. ARVN Military Police halt us while a bus crosses from the north, probably the last of the day. We rumble and clatter across, pass through sleepy Nhân Biểu, and head for the base.

The spindly-legged watch towers come into view and then the outer rolls of razor and barbed wire. I look for the dove, hoping for an omen. I don't see it. Việt and the APT chatter, too fast for me to follow.

I pull up to the gate and a helmeted MP comes out of his sandbag bunker and cautiously approaches my window, looking hard at the Vietnamese and saying something behind him to another MP still inside and just visible through the gun port in the bunker.

I lean out the window and talk fast. "The Brigade S-2 is going to meet us here with a Recon Team. We're going to assemble in the ditch on the other side of the highway. He'll drive this vehicle to the S-2 office and I'll pick it up in the morning."

The MP looks suspicious, and shouts behind him, "Have you heard anything about this?"

The other MP appears in the sandbagged doorway with a field phone at his ear. "It's OK, S-2 is on the way here with a Recon Team."

Beside me Việt is frowning. "What's happening, cố vấn? Where are the others? We need to get moving."

Lúc-Thanh leans across from the opposite window, his bad eye rolling. "He's right, cố vấn. It'll soon be dark. We need to be in position."

The Major is coming," I say.

"And the others?" Việt asks.

"Them, too," I say. "All."

"They better hurry," Việt grumbles.

"I'm going to park," I tell the MP. "Tell the Major we'll be in the ditch. Hustle them up."

"Roger that," the MP says.

I pull off to the side and we climb out and descend into the ditch. It's deep enough so we can sit in the bottom and not be seen. Việt watches the darkening sky and fidgets.

"The VC will be moving soon, cố vấn," Lúc-Thanh says. "Maybe we better go without the Americans."

Bad Jose's big face appears over the top of the ditch. "We're here."

Six Grim Reapers and Bad Jose climb down into the ditch and squat among us. Most of them I know from recon ops into the mountains.

"Major Lukitsch is informing all the security elements you'll be outside the wire," Bad Jose says. "I'll see you in the morning. Good hunting and good luck."

He hoists his heavy body out of the ditch, and we hear his footsteps crunch away. I quickly explain the plan to the Grim Reapers and then a discussion ensues about who will go on whose team, who will get the two Starlight Scope night-seeing devices, and who will carry the radio.

Bad Jose's face appears over the top of the ditch again. "I forgot to tell you. There's an outdoor USO show tonight, a Korean girls' band. You'll be hearing a lot of noise from the base."

"Got it," I say.

Việt stands up. "Cố vấn, we've got to go. It's going to be dangerous now, especially for me."

The Grim Reapers continue discussing.

"We're going," I say, and I take one of the Starlight Scopes and nod to Việt, who immediately rises up out of the ditch, crosses the highway, glances back to see that we're following, descends into the ditch on the other side, rises to ground level again, and turns into the cleared no-man's land between the base perimeter and Nhân Biểu's rice paddies and graveyard. Walking five steps behind him under the post-sunset sky, I marvel once more at how agile, silent, and alert he is, how much in his element of hunter and hunted at night.

In the distance, the railroad embankment rises black against a darkening sky. My heart races. We're moving into position way too late. Suddenly from the base there's an explosion of sound, cheering, whooping, and the Korean girl band blasting out a high-amp version of Johnny Cash's "Folsom Prison Blues."

"When I was just a bay-bee, my mama told me, son,
Always be a good boy, don't ever play with guns . . ."

As quickly as it started, the song ends to a huge roar of disappointment, either a technical-glitch power outage or an unruly crowd charging the stage, and the MPs closing the show down. Outside the wire, the world plunges back into deepening shadows and the soft sound of boots on a water buffalo path headed toward the railroad embankment.

Gliding silently ahead of me, Việt suddenly drops and lies pressed into the dirt, aiming his M-16 into the night ahead of him. From the many times I've walked behind him, I know this is not the usual drop just to listen and check things out. He's seen something. I drop, too, silently squirm up to him, and we lie together, aiming into the night.

Without turning his head and in a voice so low I can barely hear it, he gasps, "Three VC! Their first man and I almost bumped into each other. He dropped and crawled back. We both didn't shoot because the whole base will open up on all of us. We have to go back now."

I carefully unsling the Starlight Scope, turn on its soft hum, and press it to my eye. There! In the weird world of green-coated magnified starlight, I see a figure crawling backward. Or is it? I believe Việt, but I've been fooled before by Starlight Scopes' strange world of green and black, the soft hum, and the pressure of the rubber suction cup against the eye and fevered brain.

"We have to go back," Việt whispers again. "The VC won't go on to Nhân Biểu now. They're probably on the other side of the tracks already. Go back. Sleep at the base. Maybe the show will start again."

I think about it. *I don't want to go back.*

"The VC may go on to the hamlet," I whisper. "They'll think

we're just a patrol outside the base. They may circle back, cross
the stream and the graveyard, and enter the hamlet by the small
shrine. We can still get them."

"No good," he whispers. "It's too dangerous. Go back. We
can eat at the mess hall, breakfast, too."

"I'll walk first if you don't want to," I whisper.

"No," he whispers mournfully. "I'm not afraid. I'll walk first.
But we won't see the VC, only plenty of mosquitoes."

A light! A light flashes from the small shrine toward the
railroad tracks, one-two-three times! A signal, the all-clear from
the hamlet. Việt knows it, too.

"OK, we go," he whispers. "We'll circle too, and cross the
stream and graveyard, but we have to move fast. The Americans
behind us better follow."

He rises, and bending low, turns off the path and heads down
a gentle slope toward the black ribbon of the stream that flows
under the railroad bridge from the wild other side, the world
of the VC, "Indian Country." Glancing back to make sure Lúc-
Thanh is rising behind me and hoping the others are, too, I follow
Việt down to the stream.

He looks back to make sure I'm following and, holding his
rifle chest-high, steps into the water. He crosses, slowly and
silently, and I begin, boots sinking into the soft, muddy bottom
till the water is thigh-high.

Việt moves into the graveyard and I follow with my boots
sloshing. Grave mounds rise around us like small hills and there
is the feeling of spirits in the air. Việt winds his way through the
grave mounds with the dark hamlet to our left, the stream to our
right, and the railroad embankment dead ahead.

Việt goes down again, one of his check-things-out drops. I
drop too, and imagine our whole team behind me going down
like dominoes and lying still as death, waiting and wondering

what's going on up ahead. I crawl up beside Việt and we lie aiming our rifles into the night. Suddenly to our near right front, where the stream flows under the tracks, one-two-three ghostly armed forms rise from the stream bed and we, without a word, start shooting: "Babababababam!"

Noise and muzzle flashes rock the night, the ghostly forms jump, fall, dive, and disappear. We empty our magazines in seconds, reach into our pockets to reload, and before we can, a hellstorm of fire comes back at us from, it seems, every point of the compass, left, right, center, even behind, streams of bullets like metal killer bees cracking over our heads, splitting the air, seeking our flesh, bones, tissue, organs, even red tracers burning the air just inches above us, saying, "You die."

Việt disappears, just vanishes off to my left as if swallowed by the earth and the night, and I begin crawling, squirming, almost *burrowing* off to the right, knowing I have to get out of the kill zone, and that my life now hangs by a very thin thread. *I have to get to the next grave mound, lie behind it, and reload. Got to get to that next grave mound, keep crawling.*

A huge flash and roaring explosion burst just above my head, filling my consciousness, sending shrapnel through my hat and into my skull, and slamming my face into the earth. I feel I die for an instant but I keep on crawling, I will myself *through* death, squirm around the next grave mound, and lie pressing myself hard into the grazed grass of the graveyard and the sheltering earth.

Grenade explosions go off all around me now, sending waves of nausea through me and shaking the earth. Bullets are still blazing my way, seeking me, and the VC are tossing grenade after grenade. One bursts low to the ground behind me and I feel my left leg whip like a willow switch, and a warm, wet stickiness fill the inside of my boot.

I still don't feel any pain, but now I'm pretty sure I've been hit in the leg and probably the head, where my hat feels tight around my crown, as if someone grabbed my brim and pulled it down toward my ears, I think in a brief and absurd thought, *like the bully on the beach in the old Charles Atlas ads.*

The shooting slacks off but the grenades keep coming and my mind begins working at hyper-speed, weighing disastrous outcomes and possible counter-measures. *They're not sure where I am, so they're lobbing grenades in, hoping one of them gets me. Soon one will land on my back and blow a big hole. I've got to lob one on them before they lob one on me.*

Without rising even an inch, I reach back with my right hand, pull a grenade out of my pocket, curl my left forefinger into the ring, and pull the pin. I now have a live grenade clutched in my hand. *Got to lob it on them before they lob theirs in on me.*

Another grenade goes off to my right and shrapnel whooshes through the air like a scythe of death. Then silence: no shooting, no flashes, no explosions. Silence reigns on the battlefield.

They're there, I think, *listening for me, waiting for me to make a move. If I throw my grenade now, they'll hear the "ping" the spoon makes when it releases from my hand and activates the charge, and they'll know exactly where I am. Wait, don't throw!*

I clench my right fist around the grenade and hold the spoon tight. I move the grenade under my chest to add my body weight to my grip. My mind continues to run at top speed. *Now they'll come looking for me and here I lie on grazed grass with big leaves in my hat. They'll walk right up, put an AK muzzle to the back of my head, and boom, that's it! Or they'll drag me off, march me to captivity in the mountains, make me walk naked through their villages, and old ladies will come out and beat me with sticks. But no, I'm wounded, probably in the head, and I'm pretty sure in the lower leg. I don't even know if my foot is attached. It's wet down there, though I did just wade through the* stream. For sure I'd slow them down. They'll just shoot me in the head and leave me here. I could end it all before they do it, release my grip, and let the grenade go off under me. It probably won't even hurt, just a big flash and that's it. No more fears, no doubts, no guilt, no nothing. No, I don't think that's my way. But wait! Maybe I'm wounded worse than I feel, and I'm losing a lot of blood. Maybe I'll pass out from loss of blood, release my grip on the grenade, and BOOM! I'll kill myself. Got to squeeze tight, got to hold on. And pray, yes, hold on and pray. That's the only thing I can think to do. Oh God, you know I don't usually ask for things for myself, and I don't make promises about my behavior, but get me out of this, please, and I'll try to be good.

"WHOOOSH-POP!" A parachute flare streaks up from the darkness to my right and comes floating down, burning, hissing, and making the grave mounds sway and dance. I press myself harder against the grenade and the earth, thinking, Great! Now they'll see me for sure! The flare hits the ground, hisses and burns out, and the cemetery plunges into black again.

"Cố vấn!" A whisper comes out of the darkness behind me.

Việt! He survived. He's alive!

He crawls up beside me and whispers, "Are you wounded?"

"In the head and leg, I think." I pull my hand out from under my chest. I don't know how to say, "I have a live grenade here."

I whisper, "I have a grenade. Very dangerous!"

I roll on my side and hold out my hand with my fist clenched around the grenade.

"Give it to me," he says. "Like this." He puts his hands on mine and rolls the grenade into his hand, holding the spoon down all the time. Now *he* has a live grenade in his tightly-clenched fist.

"Do you have the pin?" he whispers.

I hold out my left forefinger with the ring around it and the pin dangling.

With his free hand he pulls the ring off my finger and then in a brilliant move I would not have believed possible, especially in the dark, he pushes the pin back in the grenade and drops it in his pocket.

Then, becoming the VC medic he once was, he takes off my hat, softly touches the back of my head, unlaces and gently pulls off my boot, and crawls up near my head again.

"Yes, you are wounded in the head and leg, but they're not serious. Don't be afraid. I'm going back to tell the Americans."

Without a sound he vanishes behind me and I lie there feeling alone but knowing he is doing the magic again that I saw so often in the forest and mountains. I marvel at how he could transfer a live grenade from my hand to his and put the pin back in the dark. Suddenly, something else strikes me. *He asked me, "Có pin?" Do you have the pin? If he really doesn't know English, how does he know 'pin'?" The Vietnamese word for grenade is lựu đạn . Surely there's a Vietnamese word for "pin" too. Ah, Việt, who are you, really?*

"Cố vấn!" His whisper comes out of the night and in a moment he's lying beside me.

"The Americans are calling a *chuồn chuồn* for you. After you're gone, we'll go back. We'll get food at the mess hall and beds in the barracks. Maybe the show will start again, now that the shooting has stopped. I'll bet those Korean girls are beautiful. Maybe they'll sing my song. Listen! The helicopter is coming! I'll visit you in the morning. You're going to be OK!"

He vanishes again, leaving me listening to the approaching medevac chopper. *He used the VC word for helicopter, "chuồn chuồn," or "dragonfly," and he obviously understood Bad Jose's news about the Korean girls' band. Apart from master of the arts of war, who are you, Việt?*

The noise of the chopper increases, and I twist my head and see it, a big blackbird flying over the watchtowers and wire of the base, over the stream and the graveyard, and now over me, roaring, rotors beating, slicing the air, starting to descend, and looking like it's going to land right on me!

It turns its big belly light on, brightly illuminating the world beneath it, including me. If there are any VC still around, here I am. Still it descends, looking like it's going to put its skids right on my back, a human landing pad. *What a finish to the night, to life!*

The chopper settles uneasily beside a grave mound to the right. Two crew jump out, run toward me, lift me up, belly-down, carry me to the chopper, and slide me in so I'm stretched out on my stomach from one open door to the other. They jump in, shout to the pilot, and we lift off. The ground begins to fall away fast.

Though I know the VC could still bring us down with a rocket, I feel strangely good, still no pain, enjoying the rush of cool air through the chopper's open sides, the star-bright night, the dark mountains to the west, and the mysterious, magical earth below. Then we're over the wire, minefields, and base, and descending toward the landing pad of the U.S. Army's 18th Surgical Hospital, a big red cross on the steel mesh, the chopper settling and the rotors winding down.

Four medics come running out of the hospital and they slide me out, load me onto a canvas stretcher, and run in a bent-legged, Groucho Marx-like shuffle toward the Emergency Room. I feel completely relaxed, taken care of, given up to the Hands of Fate. *God got me out of that bad situation. I even think I could walk into the ER, but I'm enjoying this feeling of* surrender.

The medics place me on a table face-down and I lie there with my chin on my crossed hands, feeling like a kid lying on a riverbank watching the water flow by. Movement catches my eye across the room and I see three female American nurses gazing in my direction. From behind me a doctor and medic approach and begin cleansing and probing my wounds. Something hurts a little. They give me a shot and I am floating again.

One of the nurses approaches with a clipboard and a pen. She bends down near my face and asks, "Can you talk?"

She's beautiful and curvaceous, with bright blue eyes, an upturned, sunburned, freckled nose, and a wisp of light brown hair falling across her forehead that she blows back with a soft puff. Her voice is Deep South and sweet as honey.

"I think so," I say in what I hope is a wounded-hero voice.

"I'm the head nurse here," she says. "I need to get some information."

Oh-oh, here it comes, I think. *What will they say and do when they find out I'm a civilian?*

"OK," I say.

Just then, tall First Lieutenant Riggs, the Grim Reaper commander, comes striding in. He nods to me and approaches the doctor, who's still bent over my leg.

Riggs says to the doctor, "He's not here."

The doctor asks something I don't catch. Riggs answers in a low voice and the doctor says, "He's wounded, isn't he? That's what we do here."

I twist my neck and see Riggs staring at my leg with a horrified look, and the color draining out of his face. He turns away and heads for the door, calling back to me over his shoulder, "We'll visit you tomorrow."

"What was that all about?" the nurse asks the doctor.

"I'll tell you later," he says, and he bends over my leg again.

"All-rightee," she says, pen poised over her clipboard, "let's get that information. Name?"

"Richard L. Stevens."

"Serial number?"

I give her my Social Security number and hope that flies. She writes it down. I guess the military is using that now.

"Date of birth?"

"May 21, 1939."

She pauses. "Thirty-one? You don't look that old."

"I lead a clean life," I say.

"Oh? What are you doing here then? Place of birth?"

"Chicago, Illinois."

"Big city boy, huh?"

"Actually, small-town boy. My parents moved to Prairie City, Iowa when I was two."

She blows the hair off her forehead again. I'm loving this and hoping she is too.

"Next of kin, relationship, and address?"

"Dorothy Stevens, mother, Box 94, Prairie City, Iowa."

"You current home address?"

"96-165 Waiawa Road, Pearl City, Oahu, Hawaii."

"I went to Hawaii on R&R. Loved it. You live there? This gets better all the time. Your rank?"

Here it comes, I think. "Civilian."

Her pen hovers over her clipboard and she stares at me. Finally she says, "Yeah, we all are at heart, but what are you really?"

"No, really, I am a civilian. I'm in the Foreign Service. I was in the Marines but now I'm out. I'm the Chiêu Hội Advisor for Quảng Trị Province."

"Hey, girls!" she calls to the two nurses across the room. "Come on over. We got us a civilian here."

They come over and flank the head nurse. The doctor and medic continue working on my leg.

"He doesn't *look* like a civilian," one of the nurses says. "What's with the face paint and camo?"

"I bet he's a spy," the second one says. "Are you a spy, Mr. Civilian?"

"You know what?" the head nurse drawls. "You are the sexiest thing we've ever had in here. And now we're going to have to cut your pants off. Snip-snip-snip, here they go." She pulls scissors from her uniform breast pocket, and brandishes them over her head.

In a flash I remember Annie and Sgt. Jones and the way his surgical scissors gleamed, and her writhing in shame below.

"Hold off now, ladies," the doctor says, and I see something like a warning look pass between him and the head nurse.

They're boyfriend-girlfriend, I'd bet on it. Shucks.

"I'm sending him down to X-ray," the doctor says.

After X-ray, a Chinese-American lieutenant gives me a Purple Heart, a medic wheels me into a ward, and I lie thinking a long time before I fall asleep. I think about Việt and the amazing things he did tonight, vanishing when the hellstorm of bullets came searching us, then rolling the grenade out of my hand and replacing the pin in the dark. I think about that strange feeling of dying when hit in the head, but crawling *through* death, willing myself to keep crawling to the next grave mound, and lying behind it as a different—or changed—person.

I hear the rumble of distant thunder, artillery or bomb strikes in the Trường Sơn Mountains. Before tonight that sound stirred me and called me to go out there, deeper and deeper into the heart of darkness. Now I knew it was over. That which had drawn me since I was a small kid in World War II, with all the "big guys" going off to serve, and in junior high during the Korean War, that urge, passion, obsession to be a warrior, to experience combat, the jungle, wild places beyond the law, senses on hyper-alert and extremes of emotion, hunting and being hunted by armed men, was over. I was different, changed. I died and was born anew.

Like Chief Joseph of the Nez Perce famously said, "I would go to war no more."

The question was, what next?

I think of Annie, wherever she is and bearing unspeakable hardships, at least in part because of me. *I realize now I fell in love with her the moment I saw her flash like a ghost across the path and crash into the bamboo, and I vow to remember her always, to tell her story, to take her as an example in whatever I have to bear, and someday to see her again, in this life or another, and tell her, "I'm sorry. I'm sorry for what we did to you and your country."*

I fall asleep to distant drums and the persistent, nagging question, *What next?*

5

THE RETURN OF ANNIE

*And, the bottom line, if you have a love for your fellow
humans, you will always feel the closeness of hearts no
matter how far away we are from each other.*

— Hoàng Thị Nữ

WHAT CAME NEXT was a slow-moving, all-consuming whirlwind
of change. I healed fast, finished my tour, said heart-breaking
goodbyes to all the brothers and sisters, lovers and friends, and
to the beloved land of Vietnam, Annie's world of mountains,
forests, rice paddies, sand dunes, thatched hamlets, and amazing,
resilient, beautiful people. Flying away for what I thought was
the last time, I felt I was leaving not only my blood, but a big piece
of my heart there. As the coastline of Vietnam receded below
me, I wiped the tears from my eyes and looked forward to the
adventures and challenges I knew were to come, all energized—
and to be endured—by the example and inspiration of Annie.

Soon after I left, I began writing, nearly every morning for
the next ten years, what became a 2,000-page manuscript about
my three years in Vietnam and the eighteen months between
my tours when I hitch-hiked and backpacked around the world.
Annie's story was prominent in what I wrote, and she was never
far from my mind as a mighty inspiration—and rock in hard
times.

I served five years in the Foreign Service in various parts of the globe and left that to live an immersed-in-nature life high in the Sangre de Cristo Mountains above Taos, New Mexico, and on Guam. I married and divorced and married again. I had three children and knew the joys of family life and the gut-tearing pain of breakup. I thought I escaped PTSD, but I was wrong.

After South Vietnam fell to the North's Ho Chi Minh Offensive of 1975, and the U.S. fled from the rooftops of Saigon in helicopters, I moved with my family back to Hawaii and returned to graduate school. I had suspended my studies in 1965 to join and then leave the Marines for a second time, teach in Japan, and go to Vietnam to experience the war. On one of my first days back in school, after telling some of my experience in Vietnam, a fellow master's degree candidate said, "You *have* to read Joseph Campbell's *The Hero with a Thousand Faces*. You'll find *your* story there."

I devoured Campbell's book on comparative mythology, in which the hero's journey, as seen in myths and religions around the world, is to be understood as the life-journey of us all. I was especially struck by three phases of the journey: "Separation from the World," "Journey to a Strange and Dangerous Land," and "Meeting with the Goddess." The last included, as well as a goddess archetype, the earth itself as "nurturing mother and inevitable bride." I knew for me, the "Meeting with the Goddess" was with Annie on the Night of Wandering Souls. *Where is she now?* I wondered. *Did she survive the horrors of the Regional Interrogation Center? Was she liberated as the South fell?*

I wrote my MA thesis and PhD dissertation on the Ho Chi Minh Trail and the latter was published as a book, *The Trail: A History of the Ho Chi Minh Trail and the Role of Nature in the War in Vietnam*. I followed that with the story of Việt's and my experiences on the Trail, *Mission on the Ho Chi Minh Trail: Nature, Myth, and War in Vietnam*.

I became a trail hunter for the Hawaii State Division of Forestry and Wildlife, searching for trails of the ancient Hawaiians using what I had learned from Việt. In the wilds of Hawaii, I often thought of Annie and her life coming down from the mountains on secret trails, and the hamlet path she burst across the moment I first fell in love with her, even as I was chasing her with a rifle in my hand. I began teaching at the University of Hawaii Center in Kealakekua on the Big Island, and in the spring semester of 1995, I jumped at the chance to teach "History of the Vietnam War."

My students were mostly "non-traditional," adults from the community who had a strong interest in Vietnam: the PTSD Counselor at the Vet Center, a librarian at our library, a Hawaiian activist whose dad was a Vietnam vet, a retired Air Force colonel who had been a helicopter pilot in Vietnam, and others. A feature of the class was telling the stories of people whose lives illustrated aspects of the war. I saved Annie's story for last and mentioned that I was writing a book about her. After class, Jerry Miki, the retired colonel and chopper pilot, waited for me outside.

"Are you planning to go back to Vietnam to look for her?"

Jerry's question caught me by surprise. "Uh, no," I said. "I haven't made any plans like that."

Still the colonel, Jerry, who was tall, handsome, fit, and mixed Chinese-Japanese, said, "Well, you *have* to go back. You can't write about her without getting her side of the story. And you have to go back soon. They don't live as long as we do!"

"You know, Jerry," I said, "I don't want to go back to Vietnam. And to tell you the truth, I can't afford it."

"What?" he said. "How much can it cost? Two thousand dollars? I'll loan you the money. I'll write you a check right now. You know I'm right, too. You can't write an honest story without hearing hers."

"I'll think about it."

"Talk to your wife. She'll agree with me. And you can pay me back whenever. No rush."

"You're a good man, Jerry."

"Don't take too long to think about it."

"I don't even know if she's alive, or if she is, can I find her, and will she talk to me?"

"You'll find her," he said. "I feel it."

And if she'll talk to me, I thought, *what will she say?*

Something else gave me pause: The Communists in control of Vietnam were still hunting down their enemies. When they took over, first on their revenge list were "ralliers," *traitors* to them. What happened to Đặng Sỹ, Lúc-Thanh, Nam, Một, Việt, and the rest—if they weren't still VC? What happened to Vinh, Lan, Chief Thuận? Hopefully they got out in time, if *they* weren't VC, too. And what would the new rulers of the country think about a former Chiêu Hội Advisor—me—coming back into their territory? I decided I wouldn't volunteer that information, though it was in my books, but emphasize my time in Huế as a Refugee Advisor. Who was I fooling? The NVA took Saigon with our computers still running. If they cared to look, they would know everything about me. And if I did find Annie, she would be able to tell them.

Still thinking about Jerry's offer, I got the old powerful feeling as I headed for home in North Kohala, the same one I had in Quảng Trị, of "surrendering to the hands of fate." Come what may, I knew I was on my way back to search for Annie.

Over the next few days I made a plan: I would write a letter to the province governor stating my purpose and have it translated into Vietnamese. I would make Huế my headquarters and launch my search from there. I had a strong feeling that if Annie was alive, she would still be in Quảng Trị just north of Huế, and in Hải Lăng, her home district. I would go in July to be there on the full-moon Night of the Wandering Souls. I fantasized that she would go with me to the stream and tell her story where it happened. I began to get more and more excited about this and pushed fears that it might be a one-way trip down in my mind.

The semester ended and Jerry wrote the check. I got a visa, and my wife gave me a special notebook in which I was to "capture it all." As July approached, I expanded the idea of the search, thinking I'd also go to Cổ Luỹ to look for the guerrilla leader Võ Công Đỗ or any of his men, and of course keep watch for Việt, though he was surely under cover with a different name, *if* he'd survived and *if* he wasn't a VC all along.

On Father's Day I got a surprise call from old friend David Oyster, an Army lieutenant in Vietnam whose dream then was to go "back to the World" and make nature films. He succeeded, working with Carl Sagan on *Cosmos* and producing nature films for National Geographic and PBS.

"Happy Father's Day."

"Same to you. How goes it?"

"I'm doing a film on Chesapeake Bay. Perfect for someone named Oyster. What's new with you?"

"Hold onto your hat. I'm going back to Vietnam to look for the woman I helped capture in '69. I'm writing a book about her."

"OK, don't say no, but I want to come with you. I'll film your search and the meeting, and you can do what you want with it."

"I don't know, David. It's pretty personal. And I don't even know if she's alive."

"Just think about it. I'll call you tomorrow."

I thought about it. We decided I'd go for one week of search and a hoped-for first meeting. Then he would come, and if it was OK with her, we'd have a second meeting.

On July 5, with the moon moving toward the Night of Wandering Souls, the elder of my sons, Lani-Minh, who was half-Vietnamese and visiting from Texas, waited to drive me to the Kona Airport. My wife Mercédes and I said our goodbyes.

"If something happens to me, that's my karma and I accept it."

"Don't say that," she said. "You're coming back. You have to tell her story."

At the airport, Lani shared a favorite quote: "'Courage is not the absence of fear but being afraid and going anyway.'"

"I guess that's me," I said. "Love you, son. I wish you were coming with me."

"I don't want to go back to Vietnam. Mom and I escaped from there as refugees, remember?"

I shouldered my big green pack and made my way to the open-air waiting area, where four Marines in camo were sprawled and sleeping. Memories flashed of the many times I spent in the Marines waiting in bus stations, train stations, airports, and aboard ships — waiting. I dropped my pack and sat down to wait.

Guessing that I'm going to be speaking a lot of French in Vietnam, I pulled out my French copy of The Little Prince and re-read its messages of love and friendship, and the fox's secret that "one sees clearly only with the heart," and "what is essential is invisible to the eyes." Part of my plan for survival was to radiate as much love and positivity as possible, to "Let my way be a blessing way," and to practice that in both the briefest and most difficult of contacts. As our Aloha Airlines flight was called for Honolulu, I wondered how that personal mantra would be tested on this trip. The Marines rousted each other up and we all walked out and climbed aboard the plane.

Honolulu was hot and humid and the hassles of checking in for the long Cathay Pacific flight to Taipei with connections to Ho Chi Minh City were many. Sweating, I kept reminding myself, "Let your way be a blessing way." This came to me from the

Navajo "Blessing Way" chant I remembered in the mountains of New Mexico the day my wife, daughter, and I left our cabin to return to Hawaii. Finally aboard, I helped the beautiful air hostess, Wu Yu-Fang by the name tag pinned to her uniform, stow gear in the overhead compartments. Sitting at last and basking in her smile and the smell of her perfume, I felt better.

Looking around and listening to the chatter, most of my fellow travelers seemed to be Vietnamese returning to what used to be their country or visiting for the first time. Next to me, Thanh, a young, tough-looking, broken-nose boxer from the rough Honolulu neighborhood of Kalihi, was nervous about his first return to the land of his ancestors. Across the aisle, a plump, well-dressed, middle-aged Vietnamese woman loaded with jewelry and perfume laid a slick magazine on my lap and said, "Read that. Very important. It's about the Supreme Master. She's a goddess. You should go see her. I been three times already."

I sat there stunned, the magazine on my lap. *Should I tell her, I'm also going to see a goddess? She was a Supreme Master, too, of war, courage, physical skills, and endurance. She had it all. I hope she's still alive and that she'll talk to me and won't want to kill me or turn me over to the police.*

I leafed through the magazine. The Supreme Master was an attractive Asian woman who was regarded by her followers as an incarnation of the Buddhist Goddess of Mercy, Kwanyin, or Quan Thê Am in Vietnamese. I started to hand the magazine back, but the woman's eyes were closed and she was meditating, her lips moving in a silent chant. Watching her lips move and catching a whisper of sound, I suddenly remembered the chant taught to me by Lani's mother, a prayer to Quan Thê Am for blessings. I said it several times and hoped Quan Thê Am was listening.

Where does that come from? I wondered. *Something I haven't thought about in years and there it is, fresh in my mind. What else is going to be touched, uncovered, spring forth and hit my emotions?*

I looked over at the woman again and she seemed to be asleep. *Going to see the goddess. We were on the same journey.* Beside me, Thanh the boxer twisted and turned and tried to sleep. For him, the goddess was the land itself, the sacred homeland waiting for his first physical connection with it. I pulled out my notebook to see what Joseph Campbell wrote about the beloved Earth as the goddess: "She is the mother that gives us birth, that nourishes every second of our lives . . . and she is the inevitable bride that receives us, open and waiting, that transforms us at the end into something new."

My mind jumped back to the night I was wounded. I thought then, and for years after, that I had died when hit in the head by the grenade exploding above me, but that I had "crawled through death," I had *willed* myself to keep moving to the next grave mound and been transformed into someone new. Later, I ascribed the saving feature of that not so much to will as to God or guardian angels, and that my life had been spared because I still had things to do, and one was to tell Annie's story.

I felt an emotional rip tide surging within me, and as the lovely Wu Yu-Fang came walking down the aisle checking on us, I reached for *Le Petit Prince* to try to gain some control.

"Everything all right here? I *love* that book." She smiled, looking at the cover.

"Me, too!"

She went on down the aisle, no doubt making other hearts flutter, and I opened the book toward the last, where the Little Prince is struck by a poisonous snake. How many times have I read this to refresh my French and yet this time a flood of tears poured from my eyes and chills raced up and down my spine accompanied by images of wife, kids, and home. *Not even in Vietnam yet and already my emotions are raw. Oh, Little Prince, why did you have to die?* Right away the answer came: *So he could return.*

We landed in Taipei and an airlines bus transported us Vietnam-bound passengers to a hotel for the night. At dinner in the hotel, I talked to a Malaysian student, May, who was reading *Wuthering Heights.* Amazingly, I remembered a line from the book that struck me as funny when I read it in the Marines thirty-five years ago. Heathcliff (I think) said it to the dogs that came out barking at him as he approached the castle: "Wretched curs! You deserve perpetual isolation from your species for your churlish inhospitality." *Try to say that to barking dogs,* I thought. *Maybe you have to be British.*

I began to see this trip as taking my mind, body, and emotions on a very long trip from my mostly laid-back life in Hawaii, opening me up to memories and stripping away layers of reserve. *What will happen,* I thought, *when finally confronting the real Vietnam, and Annie and her people, my former enemies?*

In the morning after rolls and coffee, we were transported back to the airport to board the flight to Ho Chi Minh City. Excitement, nervousness, apprehension, joy, fear—you could feel it all there, building higher and higher. *Let my way be a blessing way,* I repeated silently as the plane began to roll. *God bless all travelers and all those remaining at home.*

The cabin was mostly silent as we flew out over the South China Sea, with only occasional glimpses of blue water below, and the sky full of clouds, like my mixed feelings. Two seats away, the goddess-seeking Vietnamese lady waved her magazine at me and said, "You should go see her. Very powerful experience."

Thanh, the boxer, still beside me but now in the aisle seat, leaned his head back, closed his eyes, and clenched and unclenched his fists.

Starting from the front of the cabin, a buzz of energy and excited murmurs passed to the rear as the clouds broke and we flew over the coast of Vietnam. The sacred land was beneath us now. Whether returning to a place from which we fled or arriving for the first time in the land of ancestors, we were all in a sense coming home.

All over the plane people were out of their seats, leaning across those of us by the windows, pressing for a view of rivers, trees, jade-green rice fields, red earth, thatched houses, Vietnam!

"Everyone, please take your seats," the intercom voice said, and slowly, reluctantly, everyone did, though the cabin still vibrated with excitement.

Eyes wide, I drank it all in, thinking of the many flights I had made over this beautiful land in a variety of fixed-wing planes and helicopters, especially the first time I flew over the mountains and forests of the Ho Chi Minh Trail and fantasized about going down there and lying camouflaged beside the Trail, watching the ghost-like enemy pass. I shivered, thinking, *That wish came true! What fantasies of this trip will also? Will I find Annie? What will she say?*

The sprawl of Saigon—Ho Chi Minh City—appeared beneath us and the plane began to descend as the passengers' energy rose. Touchdown and rolling fast! *No going back now, buddy,* I said to myself as the cabin burst into applause and joyful shouts. *Get ready for Vietnam.*

The plane taxied toward the terminal and I thought, *Now come the first tests, Immigration and Customs. Will they see my name on a list and say, "Chiêu Hội Advisor, Quảng Trị, 1969-70. Take him to the Interrogation Center."*

We filed off the plane and walked toward our destiny. *Will the trip end here? This is it.*

Big green pack on my back and fat black fanny pack around

my waist, I stepped into the terminal. We shuffled toward Passport Control. *Here it comes,* beat in my head like a drum. The terminal was teeming and chaotic, with passengers, police, and uniformed officials everywhere. I was sweating and jostling, off-balance with the bulky packs.

Almost immediately a beautiful young woman in a light blue *áo dài* with a name tag identifying her as "Miss Nguyễn, Air Vietnam Ground Hostess," approached, showed me a card with my name on it, and said, "Excuse me, are you this gentleman?"

"Uh, yes."

"Follow me closely. I'm going to walk you through."

What is this? I thought. *Walk me through to where?*

"Give me your passport, please."

This didn't feel good but I did it.

She took it and said again, "Please follow me closely."

She weaved through a mass of people to the head of the long line at Passport Control and headed for a free agent at the far end. She said something to him I didn't catch and handed him my passport. He, while staring at me, stamped it, and handed it back to her.

"Now for Customs," she said, smiling and waving my passport. "Follow me."

What's going on here? I thought. *Is this the way the Communists do it now, send a smiling and lovely spider to trap the unsuspecting and unresisting fly?*

At Customs, we went again first to the head of the line and then to an end-of-the-line free agent where a young man dressed all in black seemed to be waiting for us — or me.

"Do you know Ky?" Miss Nguyễn said over her shoulder. "Thúy's husband. He recognized you from Lani's picture. Do you look so much alike? I'm Thúy's friend. The family's having a big lunch for you. Phượng works here, too. That's how we can walk you through."

She was referring to my in-laws of twenty-one years ago, Lani's mother's family. I began to understand, but how did they know I was coming?

Ky pumped my hand in greeting, said something to the Customs agent, and we breezed past him and were soon outside the terminal in another hot, chaotic world, this one of honking taxis and beeping motorbikes.

"I'll leave you here," Miss Nguyễn said. "Welcome back to Vietnam."

She said a few words to Ky and disappeared inside. I was still mostly bewildered.

"Hoa's waiting over there," Ky said, and he nodded toward a taxi stand. "I'll take you to Má's house on my motorbike. Everyone's waiting for you there. Thúy-Minh wrote us you were coming."

Hoa was my former sister-in-law; Má ("Mom") my dear former mother-in-law. Thúy-Minh ("Pure Light") was my former wife, Lani's mother. We were still friends, thank God. The past whirled around me in a kaleidoscope of changing patterns and colors. All the family lived in Huế till Tết '68, when they lost everything in the battle that lasted thirty days and destroyed much of the city. I had planned to surprise them with a visit after a day of acclimating and steeling myself for this, but it was a necessary hurdle I had to jump before the search for Annie began, no ducking or delaying it. I was swept up in the bosom of my Vietnamese family again, after parting from Thúy-Minh in 1974, a year before Vietnam fell to the Communists.

We walked toward the taxi stand and Hoa stepped out of the terminal's shadow and greeted me with hands pressed together, Buddhist-style. My eyes immediately flooded with tears and I couldn't speak.

She gripped my forearms with her strong hands and looked deeply into my eyes. "You'll always be welcome," she said. "You'll always be part of our family."

We embraced and my tears ran down my cheeks and dropped onto her shoulder. She pulled away and locked me again with her dark eyes. "No," she said. "It's all in the past. Everything that happened was destiny. You'll always be part of the family. Ky will take you to the house you bought for us after we lost everything in Huế. You and Thúy-Minh saved us, and she and her new husband saved us again after the Communists took over in '75. Everyone's waiting for you. I'll go there after I finish teaching today. We love you."

"Love you, too," I managed to choke out and she got into a taxi and was gone.

This trip is like running an emotional gauntlet, I thought, as Ky led me to his motorbike. I realized that in focusing on the search for Annie, I had avoided thinking what it would be like seeing Thúy-Minh's family again. Now I knew.

I spent the next two days in Saigon immersed in the love and care of the family and trying to get acclimated to the heat, humidity, air pollution, general chaos, and incessant horn-honking of Saigon, as everyone seemed to still call Ho Chi Minh City. My emotions continued to be raw with plenty of memory-rushes and regular workouts for my tear ducts. *I'm becoming on this trip,* I thought ruefully, *a real crybaby!*

At last it was time to launch the search for Annie. Perched precariously on the back of Ky's motorbike, unbalanced by my big packs, we weaved through the crazy horn-honking traffic to the airport. Sitting in the waiting room, I was swept by memories of other arrivals and departures over six years from 1965 to 1971, and here I was again, twenty-four years later, waiting for another flight to another destiny. Outside, where U.S. Phantom jets had parked and taxied, old hangars rusted and crumbled away, and bulbous Russian helicopters of the Vietnamese Air Force sat with long grass growing around them, looking like they'd never fly again. I saw my first bird on the trip, a swallow darting over the runway, and a woman came in selling bright yellow bananas. I bought six and stuffed them in my pack for later.

With time to kill, I went in the airport restaurant and bought a bowl of spicy chicken soup for fifty-five cents. The hot soup warmed my soul and reminded me of Quảng Trị's famous riverside chicken soup café, and I realized that I felt good, really good, for the first time on this trip.

Our flight to Huế was called and we walked through the heat, climbed metal stairs, and ducked into a Russian-made plane. We were greeted by Air Vietnam hostesses in heavenly pink *áo dài*, and one, with a cute round face, said, "Good morning!" to me so cheerily it set off another wave of tears as I plopped down and buckled up. *What is going on with me?* I thought. *What else on this trip is going to get me crying?*

We sped down the runway to liftoff and a powerfully good feeling swept over me that said, *This trip is worth it, right here and right now. We're on our way to Huế.*

Happy-face came by, checking our seatbelts. "Everything is all right?"

"*Very* all right."

"Good!" she said, and her perfume followed her down the aisle.

I locked my eyes to the window. Outside were cloud-mountains rivaling Guam's, my favorite cloud-viewing place from when Thúy-Minh and three-year-old Lani fled there as the North Vietnamese were advancing on Saigon. There were patches, then expanses of heartbreakingly beautiful blue sky, dark green forests, brown-colored, life-rich rivers, and only a few old bomb craters visible here and there. The land looked to have mostly healed itself. *How did we ever think we could dominate it with explosives, Agent Orange, and Rome plows?*

Suddenly I realized the amazingly good feeling that began at liftoff and had continued to grow was that I was falling in love with Vietnam again. I truly loved this land: rice paddies of shimmering green, thatched villages, groves of eucalyptus, bananas, coconut palms, then the blazing white sand dunes, the long, golden-sand beaches, and the sparkling sea. We started to descend and I heard the man behind me sigh, "Huế." Cultural capital of Vietnam, seat of the emperors even in the French period, a magical, mystical place: Huế!

Touchdown! Waves of emotion rolled over me as we taxied into the memory land of Huế-Phú Bài Airport. As a Refugee Advisor I was evacuated from here as a refugee myself during the Buddhist Struggle Movement against the war and the Saigon government in '66. Rolling closer to the terminal, the building that was the hospital where I too-often saw nineteen-year-old wounded Marines laid out naked for triage and I recalled the line from Erich Maria Remarque's classic novel of World War I, *All Quiet on the Western Front*, "Only in a field hospital do you see what war really is." In the Intensive Care Unit here, I visited my buddy "Doc" Green, a Navy corpsman from Nebraska, who was wounded by mortars up near the DMZ. Thinking I was going to cheer him up, I wore the wild Madras shirt and pork-pie hat he brought back as a gift from leave on extending his tour in Vietnam. I was stunned into horror-filled silence by all the tubes, the terrible tubes, coming out of him everywhere, it seemed, and the silent, sheet-covered bodies around him. All he could say was, "This is no country to fuck around in, man," and I ran outside and sat down on a sandbag and cried like a baby.

The plane stopped, the props wound down, Happy-Face said

a few words I didn't catch, and we all unbuckled and started pulling down our gear. *This is it. Huế, here we come. Destiny, we are here.* We descended metal steps and walked through heat to the terminal.

As the only foreigner on the plane, I was easy to spot. Amid family reunions and people going off to mini-vans and taxis, a thin, middle-aged man in dark pants and white shirt approached, followed by a younger woman in blue *áo dài*.

"Excuse me," he said. "Are you Mr. Stevens?"

I hitched up my old green pack. "Yes."

"I am Hoàng of the Mimosa Hotel. This is my sister, Liên. Your friends in Saigon called and made arrangements. We have a car and will take you to the hotel. Please follow us."

I squeezed into the back of their tiny car with my packs. Hoàng drove and Liên remained silent. I saw Hoàng's eyes in the rearview mirror, studying me.

"You had a pleasant flight?"

"Yes, thank you, very pleasant."

"That building we're passing was the American hospital during the war."

"Yes, I remember."

Hoàng went silent, though his eyes continued to visit the mirror. I pushed my pack over, wriggled out of range, and gazed out the window as more memories flashed by. *Neither Hoàng nor "his sister," if that was who she was, struck me as hotel people, and I was wondering if they were the police.* For the moment, the ride, the view, and memories were enough. As we turned onto Highway One, my favorite sign in all the world once stood there, a cheery "Welcome to Huế!" in Vietnamese, French, and English—filled with bullet holes. Just beyond, we passed through the hamlet we called "Ambush Alley" for the many times convoys and individual vehicles were shot at there and where the French head of the electrical station near the airport, returning to Huế too late after sunset, was ambushed, wounded, ran off the road, and tumbled out of his Renault into the ditch. The VC, coming to finish him off, stopped when he cried, *"Je ne suis pas américain! Je suis français!"* The VC bandaged him up, set him in his car, and he drove himself to Huế Hospital. I smiled, remembering I was studying French in Huế then and oh, how I redoubled my efforts, especially to say with no accent, *"Je ne suis pas américain! Je suis français!"*

Hoàng's eyes searched for me in the mirror again. "You were in Huế during the war?"

"Yes, I was the Refugee Advisor here in 1966 and '67."

"Ah, good. Refugee Advisor. Not soldier?"

"No, helping refugees."

"Very good."

Liên asked Hoàng a question too fast for me to follow and he answered in a low voice, something about refugees.

This is it, I thought. *I just launched my limited identity as the friendly Huế Refugee Advisor of '66-'67, not Mr. Chiêu Hội of Quảng Trị, '69-'70.*

The green and gloriously beautiful countryside began to change into the city. Hoàng weaved the car through traffic-clogged streets. Liên sat quietly, staring straight ahead. The Mimosa was a small three-story hotel near the Perfume River on the downstream edge of town. I struggled out with my packs. Liên left us and Hoàng walked me up narrow stairs to my top-floor room.

Outside my door on a narrow walkway that looked down on the hotel lobby, Hoàng asked, "Do you speak French?"

"Oui."

He looked relieved, then serious, and in flawless French he said, "May I ask why you're here?"

I pointed at the closed door. "Better if we talk inside."

"*Oui*," he said, and he unlocked the door.

The room was grim: a bed, one chair, and an old and silent air conditioner protruding from the wall. I dropped my packs on the bed. He turned the A/C on and it began clunking and humming noisily and moving warm air around the room. We stood and spoke in French. I pulled out the letter explaining my search in Vietnamese and handed it to him. He read it carefully and didn't give it back, then said something that chilled me to the bone.

"I'll have to take this to the Police. You will need their cooperation to find this woman. Give me your passport. I'll try to arrange a guide for you."

Here it goes again, I thought. I pulled it out of my fanny pack and handed it over. I felt naked without my passport.

He told me about a "dear friend" of his who was a professor of English literature. He wanted to introduce us. He would also take me on a tour of Huế on his motorbike at three that afternoon. He invited me to dinner at his house that evening with Liên and his wife and daughters. Then he returned to the subject of the police, "Maybe tomorrow they will come here to see you." And he went out.

I moved my packs over, laid down on the bed, and stared at the ceiling. The A/C hummed and clunked. *The search begins*, I thought. *Or will it end tomorrow? And who is Hoàng? Is he part of the police, too? Or an example of what Sister Hoa said on my saying goodbye to the family in Saigon, "The Vietnamese people will open their hearts to you."*

I went out and found a door leading to stairs up to the flat rooftop. I looked out at the nearby broad, slow-flowing Perfume River and the rooftops of a city full of some of the greatest joys, loves, and heartbreaks of my life. I found a shady place behind a clothesline strung with drying bedsheets, and with tear-filled eyes, wrote in my notebook memories here of Biển, Tom Gompertz, Dwight Owen, and "Goat" Hogan, gone way before their time. Ghosts of all those killed here before their time, Vietnamese and Americans, seemed to rise from the rooftops and labyrinthian streets. They joined over the river in my mind, and flowed down through the peaceful countryside to the sea. I wiped the teardrops from my notebook and went down to a lunch of papaya with lime and spicy chicken soup.

The next morning after breakfast and a walk along the river, I climbed to my room and found a tall, sharp-looking young man in white shirt and dark pants standing outside my door. Again I felt that chill: *This looked like the police.*

"My name is Tuấn," he said. "I'd like to talk to you about your letter. Let's go inside."

I opened the door and was surprised to see *two* chairs and a small table set between them. *Interrogation*, I thought.

We sat. The air conditioner hummed and clunked but did little against the heat. He studied me carefully, like Hoàng's eyes in the mirror, asked questions about my search, and took notes of my answers. He wrote Annie's Vietnamese name and where she was from: Hải Lăng District, Quảng Trị Province.

He closed his notebook. "When I have some news, I'll come back."

"Thank you."

He went out and I sat stunned. *Something's happening, but what is it? If Annie's alive and they contact her, how will she react? Will she tell them who I am? And if she'll talk to me, what will she say?*

I went up to my rooftop refuge where there was a strong wind—the Lao Wind—blowing from the distant blue-haze mountains and the Laotian border. I hid in a small island of shade and meditated to try to calm my raging nerves. I felt I was getting closer to Annie, but what did that mean for me? Tuấn didn't identify himself beyond his first name, but I had no doubt: he *was* the police.

Hoàng organized a Sunday trip to Thuận An Beach where the Perfume River flowed into the South China Sea. What luck! I escaped the hot, crowded city, and got to ride in the back of a mini-van between Hoàng's twin eighteen-year-old daughters, with Hoàng and his wife in front. The van was packed with a tarp, beach chairs, and beach food. One of the daughters spoke French and we chattered away while the other listened attentively and Hoàng weaved through what looked like a Sunday exodus of cars, scooters, and buses from Huế.

Outside, the gorgeous rural landscape of Vietnam streamed by, jade-green rice paddies, thatched houses, dazzling white tombs, blue skies, wind-dancing ironwood, eucalyptus, papaya, coconut, and banana trees, and pure, brilliant light. The seemingly endless golden-sand beach was a circus of sunbathers, running kids, colorful beach towels, food vendors, tarps flapping in the wind, litter galore, and at the far edges, people squatting and relieving themselves in the sand. I seemed to be the only foreigner.

We set up our tarp, broke out the beach chairs, and looked out to sea while the twins changed into matching pink bikinis behind a big towel. I walked down to the murky water where a lively shorebreak was tempting me to show off my body-surfing skills, but ominous dark shapes swirling here and there, plus a slight sewer smell were holding me back. The river, after all, flowed into the sea here and the river was, unfortunately, the sewer of Huế. The sun blazed. Kids ran past me laughing, jumped in, and were tumbled by the surf. Even the twins, delightful in pink, immersed themselves shrieking and laughing, and swam out past the break.

Wishing my immune system well, I plunged in and was soon

catching and riding foaming break after break, tumbling up on the sand and racing out again, trying to ignore the dark swirling shapes in the water or the filmy somethings occasionally wrapping around my legs. We ate, talked, snoozed, and I took a long walk north along the beach, thinking of Việt and Annie, whose missions extended all the way from the mountains down here to the sea.

Hoàng's brother came out on his motorbike and Hoàng suggested he and I ride back on the bike while the brother drove the mini-van.

"That way we can stay longer," Hoàng said, "and I'll tell you some of the history of the place."

Hoàng and I stayed till the shadows were long. We found the brother's motorbike among many others and prepared to leave with a horde of cars, buses, and bikes.

Before Hoàng kick-started the bike, he said, "I'll tell you a story of the last of the war. It happened right here. The remnants of the ARVN who were fleeing the North Vietnamese were told if they made it here, they would be picked up by boats and transported to Đà Nẵng, where they would make another stand. Many came here and congregated on the beach, waiting for the boats to come. But the boats never came and the NVA killed them all with artillery. It was a big deception and betrayal like there were many in those days, some by the Americans, some by our people. You can't imagine how difficult it was for us then. I had to go to the forest to hunt for something, anything for me and my wife to eat. Now it's better. Some people say you can still hear the ghosts moaning here at night. That's why we're all leaving now."

We mounted up. As on Ky's bike in Saigon, I felt tall, precariously unbalanced on the back of the small bike. Hoàng pushed the engine to its max speed, weaving among the others till he was in front. I held on for dear life. The river beside us was golden in the last light of day. Insects began to pelt us and I tried to hide behind Hoàng as he bent over trying to avoid the pelting and urging the motorbike on. Beside a canal with a golden-green paddy stretching to our left, the road became badly pitted and Hoàng weaved right to miss the biggest holes. Suddenly, over the whoosh of wind and clatter of our bike, a horn blared above and behind us and a huge bus began to pass us just inches away.

"Holy shit!" I shouted and I looked up to see people's heads and half-bodies hanging out the windows looking with horror down at us, some screaming, thinking any moment we were going to be drawn under the bus's wheels and be ground to pulp.

First the big front tire passed, so close I could smell its rubber, then the bus's rusted body, then the rear tires spinning, chewing, eating the road just off my left shoulder, throwing rocks into the rain of pelting insects. If I leaned slightly to the left or if Hoàng made a wrong move, we'd rub shoulders with the bus and be sucked under it. Above me, the horrified passengers screamed at the driver. Horn blaring, the great monster roared past, its back bumper narrowly missing hooking us. Before I could breathe, two girls on a shiny new motorbike sped after the bus and swerved in front of us, their back tire throwing rocks and narrowly missing us.

Hoàng shouted after them Vietnam's worst curse and he pulled off the road beside the canal so we could get off the bike and breathe in stillness beside the quiet water.

"I need a drink," he said. "And I know just where we're going to get it."

We got back on the bike. I thought of the image of the roaring, smoking monster passing inches from us with its screaming passengers, and I interpreted it as a warning: *If you survive this trip to Vietnam, don't come back.*

It was almost dark when we reached the outskirts of Huế.

Lights shone from small boats and were reflected from the river. Vietnamese music floated from a thatched-roof outdoor café. Hoàng pulled off the road and stopped.

"I'm treating," he said. "We need this."

We went inside and sat at a wooden table under colored lights. Mostly young people occupied several other tables. My appearance created the usual brief stir and then they went back to their conversations, the music, and their drinks. Hoàng ordered us two "specials."

"*C'est une specialité de Hué*," he said, as the waitress brought us two tall glasses of clear liquid half-filled with large white translucent balls.

"Lotus balls," Hoàng said, "with sweetened water."

I took a sip hoping it was not river water. I felt immediately refreshed and ready for whatever was to come next.

We sipped slowly, mostly in silence, awash in the music, the soft conversations of the patrons, and the feeling of being alive after the close call with the bus. Outside, lights floated down the river.

"This is good," I said to Hoàng and we gently clinked glasses.

"*Very good*," he smiled.

Back at the Mimosa, Liên handed me my key with a worried look. "The police were here," she said. "Looking for you."

A bolt of fear hit me, similar to the brush with the bus.

"The police?"

"Yes, Mr. Tuấn."

So he is police, I thought. *How does she know? Because she's police, too?*

"Did he say what he wanted?"

Liên glanced at Hoàng, then back at me. "He said he'll be here at 7 a.m. to pick you up."

"Did he say why?"

"No. Just that he would be here at seven."

I went up to the rooftop and looked out over the river and the city. *What rush to destiny is happening here? Are we going to find Annie or is this my last night of freedom, or life?*

I went down to my room, read, meditated, and tried to sleep. Like most nights on this trip, it was a *"nuit blanche,"* a "white night" of tossing, turning, raging nerves, high energy, and short, fitful bursts of sleep punctuated by fearful dreams.

At 6 a.m. I headed out for a quick walk along the river and a breakfast of papaya with lime, three bananas, and chicken soup from a street vendor.

The condemned man ate a hearty meal, I thought with a grim smile, and I walked quickly back to the hotel, fending off annoying pedicab drivers who wanted to pedal me around on a tour of Huế. *Can't you see I'm on my rush to destiny?* I thought with another sardonic smile. I arrived at the Mimosa at 7 to see a Russian-built, steel-gray car parked in front of a "No Parking" sign.

Here we go, I thought.

Tuấn emerged from the back and held the door for me to get in. He slid in beside me and said to the driver, *"Đi Hải Lăng."*

My heart skipped a beat. *Hải Lăng – Annie's home district.*

The driver, a black-mustached, tough-looking man with a boxer's face and thick forearms, turned his head and looked back at Tuấn. "Hải Lăng? Hải Lăng in Quảng Trị Province?"

Tuấn looked annoyed. "Go to Hải Lăng," he said again, and then something I didn't catch.

The driver shrugged his big shoulders, started the engine, and pulled into the street.

"Did you bring the money?" Tuấn asked.

"Yes," I said. My fanny pack was fat with a roll of *đồng*.

"For my office, the car, and driver," Tuấn reminded me.

"Yes, I have it."

"Good."

Tuấn lapsed into silence. He was maybe thirty, clean-cut, handsome, well-dressed, and fit. He reminded me of Tuấn the head of the Hải Lăng Intel Squad who helped capture Annie. Both he and the driver had "cop" written all over them.

Tuấn nodded toward the back of the driver's head. "This is Mr. Quy. He'll be our driver while we search for the woman."

"Yes, good," I said. My brain was surging with possibilities both hopeful and fearful. Quy was scary. His neck and trapezius were as thick as his shoulders were heavy, and his forearms as he gripped the wheel were huge, deeply etched with muscles, and rippling. *What does he do with his hands to have forearms like that?* One of my answers was, *He strangles people.* He drove aggressively too, blasting pedestrians, bicycles, ciclos, motorbikes, and cars out of his way with repeated horn-honking and fast and close approaches as if threatening to run them over. *If I'm going to be killed in Hải Lăng today,* I thought, *I'm sure it's Quy who'll do it.*

Next to me—and close—in the small back seat, Tuấn looked cool, calm, and collected. Beside him, wedged against the door, was a slim leather briefcase, and I wondered what was in it. Something about me, no doubt. *If only I knew how much,* I thought, *I'd know what to say when he starts asking questions.*

We rumbled across the Perfume River bridge with a flotilla of houseboats on the far shore, and tour boats and sampans on the river, some loaded with sand and others with coconuts, passing beneath us.

Tuấn began to question me, perhaps to confirm what he already knew, or to see how far I would go to try to deceive him.

"You were in Huế before?"

"Yes, in 1966-'67. I was the Refugee Advisor here. I worked for USAID, the U.S. Agency for International Development. I helped refugees. I also worked in Rural Development, building schools in the countryside, digging wells, helping with agriculture."

"You helped the people."

"Yes, that was my job."

Quy turned north on Highway One, his forearms rippling as he worked the wheel, and his big thumb on the horn button.

Tuấn looked west, where the blue-haze mountains rolled along the horizon. "You've been out there? The Trường Sơn Mountains?"

I feared where this was leading, but said, "Yes."

Tuấn surprised me with his next remark. "I've been out there, too, as interpreter on U.S. missions to search for Missing in Action airmen and their remains. Your government is very concerned about 2,000 MIAs from the war. You know how many MIAs we have? Two hundred fifty thousand, a quarter of a million! Even my grandmother and grandfather, killed by the French. We still don't know where they are buried."

"Yes, that's sad," I said. "My uncle was lost in the Amazon jungle in World War II. His plane and ten-man crew were never found."

"You were in the Marines?"

Here it comes, I thought.

"I was in the Marines twice," I said. "Before Vietnam. In Vietnam I was a civilian."

"Helping people," Tuấn said.

"Yes. Orphans, refugees, poor people."

Tuấn looked at me and we locked eyes. I liked him even though I knew it was possible he was taking me to Hải Lăng on a one-way ride. Quy roared up behind a cart drawn by a water buffalo and blared it out of the way.

"Why did you go to the mountains?" Tuấn asked.

This must be like being in a cage in a shark-infested sea.

"There were refugees in the mountains," I said. "The Bru tribal people. And I love the mountains. The mountains and the forests."

"I didn't like it," Tuấn said. "It was cold and wet. We slept on the ground for two weeks and ate cold food, U.S. C-rations. One morning I woke up and saw—very near—a big hairy arm wrapped around a tree. I think it was a bear."

I laughed and said, "Yes, it's a wild world out there."

Tuấn pointed northwest toward the mountains, the DMZ, and Laos. "My father was a Main Force soldier. He fought the Marines in the Battle of Khe Sanh. He was wounded and his leg was cut off. He lives now with me and my wife. Were you there?"

I felt the bottom drop out of my stomach again. *How many grievances do these former enemies have, and how many are still raw?*

"Yes, I've been to Khe Sanh, but before the battle. We took food up there to refugees."

"Food to refugees. Good."

Tuấn seemed to react to these bits of good news as if he was making a kind of balance sheet in his mind. I pulled out my family pictures, smiling wife and happy kids against a background of colorful Hawaiian bougainvillea. *Won't it be harder for them to kill me if they know I have a family?*

Quy roared up close behind a bus and leaned on his horn. Frightened-looking faces peered out the back and Quy shook his big-knuckled fist and forearm menacingly out the window. The faces turned to the front, the bus pulled over to the shoulder, and Quy sped around it, still blowing his horn.

"Very nice," Tuấn said, handing back the photos. "My wife and I have one son, and another child is coming."

"Congratulations," I said. "Please show me their pictures some time."

Create a future, I thought, *and maybe you'll have one.*

RICHARD L. STEVENS

"I can show you now," he said, and he pulled out his wallet and extracted a photo. His wife was attractive and smiling, the baby round-faced and plump. I thought of Vinh and Lan. *If they survived, they're probably grandparents now.*

"Very nice," I said. "Thank you."

I'll try this, I thought. I pulled out of my fanny pack copies of two of my writings: "Nature and War" for the *Veterans for Peace Journal* and "The Role of Nature in the Vietnam War" for the *Newsletter of the Society of Environmental Historians.*

"This was one of my big lessons from the war," I said as I handed them to him. "We fought against nature and lost, and your side worked with nature and won. The mountains and forests were on your side."

He took them and began to read. "This is very interesting," he said. "Nature and war: I never thought of this before. May I keep these to show my father and to some of my colleagues?"

"Yes, gladly."

Yes, buy time. I thought. *Create a future.*

"I know some professors who want to talk to you. I'll arrange a meeting for when we're back in Huế. They're especially interested in your sources."

"Yes, good." Again, I felt a chill of fear go through me, for me, and this time also for Việt. *Or was Việt a VC all the time? Was he alive? Would he suddenly appear and shout, "Cố vấn!"?*

Quy blasted his horn and blazed around another bus, muttering curses as we passed. We crossed a bridge into Quảng Trị Province and my excitement mounted as we neared Hải Lăng District Headquarters, where we took Annie after her capture.

"You know," Tuấn said in a warning tone, "you cannot do this search alone. Don't try it, whatever the results are today. Government officials might misunderstand. You have to do it with me or not at all."

"Yes, I understand."

We pulled off the highway at the bustling Hải Lăng Market and parked at the District Headquarters. I looked out the window for the dungeon where Annie was held, but didn't see it. A large sign beneath eucalyptus trees listed a hundred "Hero Mothers" in the District who lost one or more children fighting the War of Liberation.

Tuấn reached for his door handle. "You stay here. I'll enquire for Miss Nữ inside."

Quy got out, too, as if he didn't want to be in the car with me. He walked to the shade of the eucalyptus and lit a cigarette. Tuấn disappeared inside. I sat waiting, thinking, *Is she alive? Will we find her? Will she talk to me?*

Tuấn came out accompanied by a young man in sunglasses with a worn file folder under his arm. The newcomer got in the front seat. He and Quy seemed to know each other. Tuấn slid into the back.

"This is Mr. Đoàn," Tuấn said, "from the District Committee. He says Mrs. Nữ is alive and lives in Hai Quê, her home hamlet. The District Committee has given its permission to talk to her. We'll go there now."

Electricity surged though me. She's alive! If this is real and they're not driving me out to the countryside to shoot me, I'm going to see her soon. *But will she talk to me and what will she say? Will she tell them I was the Chiêu Hồi Advisor in Quảng Trị? Or do they know this already? For now this is enough: she's alive and we're going to see her.*

Quy backed out and took the dirt road we brought Annie in on, jammed in the back of my Scout. The countryside was radiantly beautiful, with rice blowing in the Lao Wind, blue skies, grazing water buffalo, picturesque houses, family tombs, and rice-drying yards. Quy drove fast, trailing dust, and talked with Đoàn, too fast for me to follow.

Đoàn raised his sunglasses, looked back at me, and asked Tuấn, "Does he know about the 100 Hero Mothers?"

"I explained to him about the sign. He knows some Vietnamese."

"Tell him we have more than one hundred now. American bombs and shells from the war are still killing our people, especially children."

"Did you understand him?" Tuấn asked.

"Yes, the war goes on," I said. "I hope your children and mine can some day meet in peace."

Quy blew his horn at an approaching buffalo cart. A woman with two large cans of sloshing water hanging from her carrying pole got off the dirt road as we blasted by and our dust cloud rolled over her.

We drove on this road from the old church, I thought, *racing through the night with Annie. Now we go back to find her.*

Suddenly in a series of images, I had this fantasy: *Annie agrees to go to the stream and tell me her side of the story where it happened on the coming night of the full moon. We walk through the bamboo where she crashed through and stand on the bank. She turns to me, smiles, and says, "Now, you jump." And she pulls out her K-54 pistol.*

Quy turned off the road and stopped at the narrow gate that led into Hai Quê Hamlet. Tuấn and Đoàn got out.

"You wait here," Tuấn said, and he and Đoàn went through the gate, Đoàn still clutching the faded folder under his arm. Quy got out without a word, stepped into a bamboo grove, and lit up, his forearms bulging and twitching like he wanted to squeeze something, probably my neck.

I sat in anticipation, my heart beating fast. Tuấn and Đoàn came back, walking quickly in the heat.

"She's moved," Tuấn says. "The people think she lives in

Quảng Trị City now. We have a possible address."

Will we find her? I thought, as Quy got back in the car and we kicked up dust on the road back to Highway One, then north through the dunes and scattered bushes and trees toward Quảng Trị City, with every mile packed with memories and the nagging question, *Or is this a one-way trip for me?*

With Quy blasting vehicles and people out of our way, Tuấn leaned toward me and said, "I've been reading your book, *The Trail*. My wife and I read a little each night and I tell my father about it. I like what you wrote. They do, too. They want to meet you."

"Good," I said, but my emotions were raging. *If he reads it carefully, he has to know who I was. Is he pretending not to know? And why?*

"If you were out of the Marines and the Refugee Advisor, why were you on the operation to capture Miss Nữ?"

I decided to try to keep the fiction alive. "Old Marine friends were on that operation. I wanted to experience the war."

"You wanted to kill someone?"

"No, especially not a girl, a young woman. I felt bad for her."

"You felt bad for an enemy?"

"I felt bad for a female human being. And I admired what I saw her do to try to avoid capture."

He fell silent as Quy pulled off the highway and drove down a straight road bordered by newly-built houses and a large, pock-marked stone wall.

"What place is this?" I asked.

"Don't you recognize Quảng Trị City?" Tuấn said. "You have been here."

"Nothing looks familiar. Nothing."

Quy stopped before a large open area and he and Đoàn discussed directions.

"This was Quảng Trị Citadel," Tuấn said. "Now it's gone, all gone with most of the rest of Quảng Trị City. B-52s bombed the city after we liberated it in 1972. That long wall you saw back there was part of a school. It's the only thing left. The Province Committee decided to leave it standing as a remembrance."

"This was the Citadel?" I said, looking around at the broad, grass-grown, open space.

"Older than Huế Citadel, part of our culture, and all gone. Bombed to nothingness."

On the far side a young couple walked hand-in-hand on the grass while a small child ran ahead.

"Before, a fortress; now it's a place to walk," Tuấn said. "In the cool of the day, more people will come."

I tried to picture where my house was, with its barbed-wire fence, walls, and sandbag bunkers beside the Citadel moat. All points of reference were gone. I felt a huge emptiness and sadness. We did this, we obliterated a relic, part of Vietnam's cultural legacy.

Quy and Đoàn discussed directions and we squeezed down a narrow street. Quy shouted a question out the window to an old man on a bicycle and the man, looking fearful, stammered an answer. Quy turned down an even narrower street and stopped by a house mostly shrouded by young citrus trees and a garden of in-the-ground and potted plants. A fresh breeze set leaves dancing.

"We think this is her house," Tuấn said.

I was swept by waves of emotions. I felt in a strange daze, a kind of dream-state. *Is this really happening?*

We got out and Tuấn, Đoàn, and I walked through the garden toward the house. Neighborhood kids started following us, saying in excited voices, "*Người Mỹ!*" American!

Quy stayed by the car and fiercely shouted, "*Đi!*" at them.

"Go!"

A tall, raw-boned man appeared at the door and looked at us with astonishment.

"We're here from the District Committee," Đoàn said. "Is this the home of Mrs. Hoàng Thị Nữ?"

"She's my wife," the man said, his eyes fixed on me with a mixture of puzzlement and hostility.

My emotions were raging. I felt in a vortex of whirling, dizzying energy.

"Is she in the house?" Đoàn asked. "We'd like to talk to her."

Three small children emerged from within the house and peeked around the legs of the tall man. The eldest of them whispered, "*Người Mỹ!*"

"Yes, she's in the house," the man said.

My heart pounded. *She's here!*

"May we come in?" Đoàn asked.

The man stepped aside and we entered the house. As we did, Annie emerged from a back room. She was older and thinner but still emanated grace and strength. Our eyes met and I saw a flash of recognition, which she immediately suppressed. She lowered a blank wall across her face and turned to Đoàn and Tuấn. "Who is he and what is he doing here?"

"He was there the night you were captured," Tuấn said. "He's a professor and he's writing a book about you. He wants to hear your side of the story."

Four young women emerged from the back of the house and gathered around Annie. Two were obviously teens and two seemed in their early twenties. All were slim and pretty. Potted plants filled the house, and doors and windows opened to the garden outside. Framed red and gold documents looked down from the walls, with Hồ Chí Minh's picture and Annie's name prominent on them. Outside, Quy shouted, "*Đi!*" again at the neighborhood kids. Annie avoided looking at me and focused on Đoàn and Tuấn.

"My story?" she said. "What story?"

"Of what happened that night," Tuấn said. "And after."

Silence. You could hear a pin drop in the room. Even the children seemed to be holding their breath, waiting for her answer.

Annie swung her attention to Đoàn. Ever the good Communist, she said, "Does the District Committee authorize this conversation?"

I realized I was holding my breath, too, waiting for her answer, and now Đoàn's.

"Yes," Đoàn said. "This conversation is fully authorized."

Annie gestured to a large wooden table under the framed documents. "Let's sit there," she said. "Daughters, bring tea."

The four girls disappeared in the back of the house while we sat at the table. Ever more in a strange, whirling energy-daze, I tried not to stare at Annie continuously, while she avoided looking at me completely. The girls brought tea in mismatched, stained glasses and we sipped while I wondered, in a fleeting thought, if mine might be poisoned. The family gathered around, standing, hushed, and waiting. Quy's "Đi!" burst again outside, chasing neighborhood kids away from the car and the house.

The husband made a short, formal welcome speech. Tuấn translated and the husband smiled at me, a gesture I returned with relief. He looked strong and I imagined he, like Annie, was a good VC. Some of the framed documents obviously bore his name. I liked him and felt we already connected on some unspoken level.

Annie glanced at me, then turned to Tuấn. "I want to know more about who he is and why is he here. Does he speak Vietnamese?"

"Only a little," I said in Vietnamese, hoping to catch her attention.

She didn't look at me.

"He understands much," Tuấn said. "But I will translate everything. This is required by the Province Committee. All conversation has to go through me."

"Then please answer my questions," Annie said. "Who is he and why is he here?"

"He was the Refugee Advisor in Huế," Tuấn said. "But he also wanted to learn about the war. He had been in the Marines, but not in Vietnam, and an old friend was on the operation to capture you. He was visiting a friend."

Annie again glanced at me. "He was visiting a friend to capture, maybe kill me?"

"When he learned it was an operation to capture you, he felt bad for you."

I sat there stunned. *Tuấn was putting me in the best light possible, ignoring what I believed he knew well. At any moment I expected to hear her say, "Not true! He was the Chiêu Hội Advisor! His 'good friends' were that band of traitors!"*

She looked at me briefly across the table. Again, I saw that flicker of remembrance before she dropped the wall. Why was she not exposing me now? She fixed her gaze on me again and I held my breath. "How did you feel when I was captured?"

"I felt bad for you, and I was afraid for what was coming."

"I was the enemy."

I shrugged my shoulders and felt my eyes moisten. "Nevertheless, I felt bad for you."

We all sipped our tea and I pulled out my notebook. "Do you mind if I take notes?"

"Don't write the book about me," she said. "I'm no one special. In the war you could find heroes everywhere. Write about the Vietnamese woman, whom Uncle Hồ has called 'loyal, defiant, and courageous.' Vietnam has a long tradition of woman warriors and woman heroes. Write about that."

Pen poised, I asked, "Please tell me when you joined the VC."

The family moved in close as she began to tell her story. Her husband — and all of us — gazed at her in awe. She told essentially the story I heard before but left out the part about the police repeatedly taking her at eighteen to Hải Lăng for questioning.

"I trained in the mountains, but my main base of operations was in Hải Lăng District. I went often on secret paths between the lowlands and the dense forests of the uplands. My main motivation was always that I loved the land and I believed in Uncle Hồ's inspiring words, 'Nothing is more precious than independence and freedom.'

"I worked hard, joined the Party, and was given many responsible positions. I mostly did political and humanitarian work, rather than fighting with a gun. All went well until the Night of Wandering Souls in 1969, when I was betrayed and captured. I saw my betrayer on the street recently. He wouldn't look at me. I didn't say anything to him. He betrayed me for money to get married."

Đoàn jumped in after Tuấn's translation. "What is his name and where does he live?"

I shivered inside. *This was a fear I had before leaving, that my search would open old wounds, bring trouble or doom to people in hiding.*

"It's all in the past now," Annie said. "I let it go. He was in prison for eight years after the war."

"Please tell us what happened that night," I asked.

What looked like Annie's eldest daughter shooed the children outside to play and the rest of the family tightened their ring around the table.

"I was in my secret tunnel across the stream from Miss Đôi's house. She was my contact in the hamlet. We knew each other since we were young. The entrance to my tunnel was underwater. I dug it myself. It came up under a banana grove on the bank across from Đôi's house. Đôi's family had a small boat for fishing. Fishermen on that stream knock on the sides of their boat to get the fish moving toward their nets. Đôi and I had a special rhythm of knocks to communicate that there were no Saigon or American soldiers around. I heard her signal and came out. She had food, water, and dry clothes for me. It was almost midnight. I heard a dog bark and felt something was wrong. I went to my other secret tunnel in the house of the uncle of my betrayer. Soon after I entered it, I heard the shouts of the Saigon soldiers calling for me to come out and 'rally,' as they called it. I opened the secret back door of the tunnel and threw a grenade at them. I ran across the path and through the bamboo bordering the stream. One man chased me and began shooting. Others ran across the bridge and shot from there. I jumped into the water and began swimming for the other side. The man chasing me kept shooting. His bullets were hitting all around me. I thought I was going to die any second, but I didn't care. I just kept swimming for the opposite side. I made it but fell and got up and started running. The soldier's bullets kept hitting all around me. I thought I was getting away, but one of the soldiers who crossed the bridge fired an M-79 grenade at me and it knocked me unconscious and wounded me in my ear."

Annie paused and pulled at her left ear, where the V-shaped chunk was missing. Again I saw Sgt. Jones's surgical scissors flash and her blood spurt. Childrens' shouts floated in from outside. A breeze blew through the trees in the garden.

"The next thing I knew, a strong man was carrying me across the bridge. He put me down in a buffalo shed and they tied my hands and feet to a bamboo pole. They got Miss Đôi and another girl from the hamlet to carry me to the old church. There they loaded me into a kind of closed jeep. There were Americans there. They took me to Hải Lăng. I think I have to stop here for a while."

"Ask her if she's tired," I said to Tuấn.

He translated and she looked directly at me, smiled mischievously, and said, "No, I'm not tired. Are you?"

"Show her your family pictures," Tuấn said.

I eagerly pulled out the pictures of wife and kids and they went around the table, creating a chorus of "ooohs," "aaahs," and "Very beautiful!"

"This boy," Annie said, pointing at Lani's picture, "looks almost Vietnamese."

"Yes, he's half Vietnamese," I said.

"Hmmm," she said, nodding knowingly.

Thankfully, she asked no more.

"Tuấn," I said, "tell her about David coming and how we'd like to invite her to go to Vinh Dinh Bac and tell her story by the stream so David can film her."

She listened closely, smiled at me again, and said, "You and your friend are welcome here any time, but my health is not so good for a trek to Vinh Dinh Bac. Your friend can film, and we can talk here."

"Thank you," I said and in what I felt was the warm glow of the moment, I dared to reach my hand toward her across the table. Though I feared rejection, she grasped my hand in both of hers and held on.

Her hands felt warm and strong and her gaze was direct as she said, "I wish for your children and grandchildren a life of peace, and that Americans and Vietnamese can meet in the future in friendship, even love."

I choked back a tide of emotions and felt tears rising within me. I wished the same peace and love for her and then as we released hands, I made a major blunder, knowing it as it came out, but unable to stop it, unhinged perhaps, by her smile, and the warmth of her hands.

"Tuấn," I said, "ask her if she remembers our conversations in the hospital and prison."

Tuấn looked surprised. "You talked to her after she was captured? And she talked to you?"

I wished I could take it back but it was too late. "Yes," I said, "several times."

He looked uncomfortable but asked anyway. A cloud passed over her face and I saw the wall fall again as she answered and Tuấn translated. "She says you're mistaken. That didn't happen."

"Yes," I said lamely. "I must be mistaken."

She smiled again, reviving me somewhat, and we walked to the door, everyone shaking hands.

"Remember," she said, "you and your friend are welcome. By the way, this is not the 'old friend' you went to see on the night I was captured?"

"No, no," I said, laughing and trying to gauge her intent. "He only shoots with his camera."

"If we can laugh about that night," she said, "we have come a long way."

We drove back to Huế mostly in silence, except for Quy's blowing everyone off the road.

At the Mimosa, Tuấn's last words were, "I'll tell you when the talk with the professors about sources is arranged. We'll do it before your friend comes and we go back to see Mrs. Nữ."

"Yes, certainly," I said. "I'll be ready. Thanks for everything today."

"It was very special for me, too," he said. "I learned a lot."

Quy drove off, his forearms bulging as he gripped the wheel and his big thumb active on the horn button. I went up to the rooftop to try to process everything. My emotions were a whirl and my nerves felt shot, but I was elated, too. It had been a day of miracles. She was alive, we found her, and she talked to me. She smiled at me and took my hand in hers. I met her family and showed her pictures of mine.

The sun sank, the river turned golden, and then slowly to black. Lights floated and shimmered: houseboats, riverside cafes, and open fires. The moon, one night from full, rose over the rooftops and floated in the dark, slow-moving water.

Suddenly a huge explosion rocked the black world downriver and blew my memory to another Huế rooftop in 1966, the house of my friend and colleague on the Advisory Team, Tom Gompertz, the Rural Development Specialist, he of the hearty laugh and one of the most brilliant people I'd ever met. I was sharing with Tom the sad news I'd just received of the death of my adopted Hawaiian dad, aloha-filled Joe Mahi, and a huge explosion suddenly rocked the city. Two years later, in Tet '68, when the VC and NVA took the city, Tom was killed, and soon after, joyful and equally brilliant Biến was taken from his house and killed too. *Oh, Huế,* I thought, tears flowing freely again, *city of great loves and massive heartbreaks.*

The moon looked down on me, a tiny figure weeping on my rooftop. To recover, I thought of the day with Annie. Her touch, like Má's and Hoa's in Saigon, felt *healing*.

The next morning at 7 a.m., as I returned from breakfast and a walk along the river, Tuấn was standing outside my door.

"Good news!" he said. "My friends, the professors, can meet with you today. I'll come here at 2 p.m. for you. My wife has arranged for a conference room at the hotel where she works."

"Ah, good," I said, though my insides were going to jelly.

I read and meditated, trying to calm my nerves. Annie did not give away anyone to her inquisitors, and I would try to do the same. Apart from not wanting to bring harm to others, I didn't want to bring any more bad karma to myself.

Tuấn arrived promptly at two, Quy behind the wheel, as usual totally ignoring me. We drove along the river and stopped at the entrance of a small, recently-built hotel. Tuấn walked me to a room where there was a long table with one chair on one side and three chairs on the other. He directed me to the one chair and sat facing me on the other side.

"They'll be here soon," he said, gesturing to the empty chairs. "They're probably in class."

"No doubt," I said, my insides still jelly.

The door opened and two heavy-set men entered. They were dressed like Tuấn in white shirts and dark pants, older than he and tough-looking. They looked nothing like any professors I'd ever seen. They shook my hand perfunctorily with no warmth, friendliness, or the exchange of names or cards. We all sat. I felt lonely on my side of the table. Tuấn, with whom yesterday I felt a rapport building, now seemed like one of them. They studied me carefully.

The older of the two spoke, more to Tuấn than to me, and Tuấn translated. "Where did you get your information on the location of the Ho Chi Minh Trail?"

I remembered reading Rang's reports on Annie's interrogations, and knew she told half-lies and partial truths, which compromised no one and gave away nothing. I decided to do the same, to speak a bit faster than usual, and to use as much "academese" as possible.

"I went to Washington, D.C. to the National Archives and looked through the files there. I also went to the Marine Corps Museum in Washington, and the Army Library in Carlisle,

Pennsylvania, and read the reports of reconnaissance teams and other assets that were used to search for the Trail."

Tuấn translated all this with difficulty and the two "professors" frowned.

"What human sources did you use?"

Tuấn, if he was closely reading and understanding my book, knew the answer to this. But with Annie in mind, I kept on the same track.

"I used myself. I got grants from the Army and Marines and traveled from Hawaii to Washington and Carlisle. I did all the research myself. Oh, and I also went to the Air Force Museum in Maryland."

Tuấn looked at me puzzled. His English was good, but this was taking him into new territory. "Would you go over that again? What are 'grants'? And please say those place names again."

We discussed in English while the two scowled and waited. The younger one took notes on Tuấn's halting translations, and often asked for clarifications.

The older one bored in again. "What documents do you have that we could see?"

"No documents can be taken from those sites. I looked at all original documents and those have to remain as part of their collections. Those are primary sources and are carefully guarded. I went away only with notes, and those are all in Hawaii."

Tuấn asked me more questions before venturing his translation. The younger one struggled again with his note-taking.

The older one asked, "What did you do in Huế in 1966-67?"

"I was the Refugee Advisor. We helped people who had lost everything. I also worked in Rural Development, building schools and digging wells in the countryside. And I was the

Youth and Sports Advisor for Huế. I organized what we called the Huế Olympics in 1967, when Vietnamese athletes and U.S. Marines competed in many sports."

"He helped people," Tuấn said before beginning the long translation.

The two "professors" seemed unmoved. Nevertheless, something strange was happening here, as it had at Annie's the day before. A cloud, a bubble of unknowing, seemed to have formed around my having been the Chiêu Hội Advisor in Quảng Trị in 1969-'70 and all the sources, experiences, and connections I had then.

May it last, I thought, *for David's visit and a few more days, at least.*

The questioning went on, returning often to sources and with my answers ever more convoluted and difficult to translate. Finally, it was over. Tuấn dropped me off at the Mimosa and I went up to my rooftop refuge exhausted, nerve-blown, and wondering, "What's going on here?" It seemed that all they'd have to do is "turn up the corner of the rug," and they'd see everything they wanted to know. But still there was that strange cloud, that bubble.

Okay, David, this is the world you're landing in tomorrow.

The moon rose full over the rooftops and river. Twenty-six years ago tonight, on this Moon of Wandering Souls, we went heavily armed to catch a girl, a young woman named by us Annie—and in some strange way, we, or I, at least, were captured by her. Like most nights on this trip, I hardly slept. I read, meditated, tried to cool down, and finally fell into a fitful slumber.

In deep night, I awoke with a start and the powerful feeling of a woman standing at the foot of my bed. I sat up, shook my head, rubbed my eyes, and tried to clearly see her. She vanished before I could discern who it was but was left with the strong impression of a spirit woman standing at the foot of my bed. *Who was she? What did it mean? Or was I going over the edge?*

At 6 a.m. I went up on the roof to exercise and watch Huế start to hum, then down for breakfast and to meet Hoàng and Liên, who had the mini-van we went to the beach in, to pick up David and his equipment at Phú Bài. Today David would film around Huế, then tomorrow back with Tuấn to see Annie, and out to Vinh Dinh Bac Hamlet to film where she was captured. I could hardly wait to see her again, to sit at her table, and hear the rest of her story.

We drove through Ambush Alley and arrived at Phú Bài just as the plane from Saigon landed.

"*Trời ơi!*" Liên said when I pointed David out getting off the plane. "Good heavens! He's a giant!"

David was 6'1" and 210 pounds, loaded with camera gear, and already filming as he walked toward the terminal.

"Don't let his bulk fool you," I said. "He has studied yoga in L.A. with Kareem Abdul-Jabbar, the *very* tall basketball player."

"David!" I shouted. "Over here!"

Sweating already, David crunched into the mini-van with all his gear. I squeezed in beside him.

"This is just about unbelievable," he said. "Is this really happening?"

"Hoàng and Liên have arranged a dragon boat for us," I said. "We're going upriver today to the emperors' tombs."

"Great! What about Annie? Did you find her? Is she alive?"

"Tomorrow at 7 we leave for Quảng Trị. You'll get to meet her whole family."

"Amazing! Tell me all about it."

We talked a mile a minute as the Vietnamese countryside passed by.

"I'm eager to capture all this," he said. "Most of what I do now is producing and directing and I miss the camera work."

"Do you like Vietnam?" Liên asked from the front.

"I *love* Vietnam," David said with a grin. "That's why I'm here. That and the chance to spend time with my ol' buddy here, and maybe most of all to meet and film Annie."

"Annie, it's an American name?"

"It's the name U.S. intelligence gave Miss Nữ," I said. "Annie Oakley was a famous woman of American history. Her skill with guns was legendary."

"Oh," said Liên. "I don't like guns."

David laughed. "Neither do I. The only shooting I did here was with a camera. I worked for Armed Forces Radio and TV in Saigon. This is my first time to Huế."

Hoàng slowed as we entered Ambush Alley. Kids ran out shouting, "*Người Mỹ! Người Mỹ!* American! American!"

"Looks like some things don't change," David said. "Remember the sensation we created when we drove to your wedding in full traditional Vietnamese wedding dress? That was amazing. I felt if we could have driven all over the country like that in that sweet '64 Chevy, the war would have ended right then and there. It created that much joy in everyone who saw us."

Hoàng geared down as a buffalo cart pulled out in front of us.

"Wedding?" Liên said, turning to look back at me. "Richard was married in Vietnam? To a Vietnamese?"

"Yes, in a Buddhist pagoda outside Saigon," I said. "With the war going on not far away. It was a beautiful ceremony. A butterfly landed on my shoulder when we were taking pictures in the garden. Everyone thought it was my mother, who had died just three weeks earlier."

Hoàng eased around the buffalo cart, "The woman in your

family pictures is not Vietnamese," he said in the best English I'd heard him use.

"Thanks a lot, David," I muttered. I leaned forward and said, "No. We were married three years. We're still friends. I visited her family–our family—in Saigon. They were the ones who called you. We have one son, Lani-Minh. He drove me to the airport in Hawaii."

"Hm," Liên said.

Huế's traffic, noise, and energy began to enfold us.

"I'm very excited about being here," David said.

"Hm," Liên said.

"Your dragon boat leaves at 10," Hoàng said. "We've packed you some lunch. I'll drive you there."

We pulled up to the Mimosa.

"Your English is *very* good, Hoàng," I said. "I'm surprised."

"*Je préfere français*," he said. "I prefer French. And I guess we all have our little secrets."

"Or big secrets," Liên said, and she got out and went into the hotel.

"I'll show you to your room," Hoàng said. "We'll meet back here at 9:45. Be ready for adventure."

"I'm always ready for that," David said. "And I'm very happy to be here."

May it continue, I thought.

We spent all day on the Perfume River, landing at temples, pagodas, and emperors' tombs, with David filming all, including the fascinating human life on the river and the lush vegetation on its banks. Memories flowed with the current and crowded the present in my mind, of the eighteen months I lived in Huế, the loves and heartbreaks I found here, the friends made and lost to the war.

"Tomorrow," I said, as we disembarked back in Huế, "it's

north to Quảng Trị to see Annie and then into the countryside to visit where she was captured."

"I can hardly wait," he said, "I can't tell you how good it feels to be behind the camera again. I'm getting great stuff, I feel it."

We talked outside my door.

"Liên is taking us to her favorite restaurant tonight. Its name translates as 'The Rice from Hell Café.' It's super-popular with the locals. She took me there once and it's a crazy-wild atmosphere, but the food is great."

"She likes you. I can tell."

"Purely Platonic," I said. "I've been helping her with her English. And I'm not endangering this trip with any bad-karma behavior. I also believe that Liên and Hoàng, if they're not police themselves, are definitely connected to the power structure here. I even feel I'd be betraying Annie if I did anything out of line."

David smiled. "I can see the lady has been a good influence on you."

"She has been an inspiration to me since that night twenty-six years ago."

"Now I get to come under her spell, too."

"It will happen. I guarantee it. By the way, we'll be going up there with the police. They're plainclothes, but they're cops."

"And that's good, I assume?"

"So far, so good. I like Tuấn. Quy is scary. Don't break any laws."

David laughed. "I won't even jaywalk!"

"That could get you killed here."

"Oh, yeah, the traffic –"

"No, Quy. Wait till you see his forearms. Like Popeye's."

"Here comes Liên. Let's have a good time."

"Then hopefully, sweet dreams. And no night visitors. I'll tell you later."

At 7 a.m. Tuấn and Quy pulled up in a mini-van. Tuấn got out to shake David's hand. Quy stayed behind the wheel not looking at us, and rubbing his knuckles as if he was itching to hit something.

"We'll stop at the market first," Tuấn said, climbing into the back. "You can buy gifts for Mrs. Nữ and her family, special fruits, now in season. Quy will go in for us."

"Good idea," I said.

We crossed the river bridge and headed for the big morning market. Tuấn wasted no time in getting David's story.

"You were a lieutenant in the Army. Did you see much combat?" David tore his gaze from the swirling world outside and smiled. "Fortunately, I saw none. I worked for Armed Forces Radio and TV in Saigon. The closest I got to combat was hearing artillery and bombs in the distance at night. We called it 'Saigon Thunder.' I had no desire to be in combat."

Tuấn nodded at me. "Unlike your friend, Richard Stevens."

"Yes," David said. "Unlike my friend. But I think he learned some things from Miss Nữ."

"And now here we all are because of that. Most Vietnamese believe strongly in destiny. Give me money. I'll send Quy to buy what we need."

Quy parked in a "No Parking" zone at the market entrance, and we handed several bills to Tuấn, all with Hồ Chí Minh's picture on them. He handed them to Quy and said something I didn't catch. Quy got out without a word and disappeared inside the bustling market. Passersby saw us and bent down to stare till Tuấn said, "Đi!" and waved them away.

Tuấn reached in his pocket and pulled something out which he kept concealed in his hand. "I've continued to talk to my father about you," he said. "He's more and more interested in your writings about nature and the war. He believes you are right. Nature was on our side. He respects that you were in the Marines and asked me to give you this."

He opened his hand. It was a brass medal with a red and gold piece of cloth attached, and an engraved picture of Hồ Chí Minh.

"My father got this medal fighting the Marines at Khe Sanh. He wants you to have it. He hopes to meet you soon."

Tuấn closed my hand around the medal. It pulsated in my hand. Tears welled up in my eyes. I fought back the feeling that I would burst.

"It's a very precious gift," Tuấn said. "He's very proud of it."

"Yes," I said, still feeling its energy pulsate in my hand. "Yes, it is. Please say 'thank you' from me and that I hope to tell him how special it is face-to-face."

"I will certainly do that."

Quy came back with two big bags. Tuấn said something and we headed out again on the broad avenue bordering the river.

Tuấn looked at us as if he had something important to say. "David, see those gray buildings across the river?"

David leaned forward and looked past me where Tuấn was pointing. *I felt a cold chill wondering where this was leading. My greatest love in Vietnam, a forbidden and dangerous love, lived in one of those buildings. Surely Tuấn does not know about this.*

"It's a hotel now, but during the war it was a residence for professors of Huế University and their families."

Oh, my God. Where was he going with this?

"Yes?" David said.

"This is a story that shows good things can come out of war, just like we were discussing with Mrs. Nữ and her example for Richard."

David looked bewildered. Blasting his horn, Quy turned north on Highway One. We left the gray buildings behind. I was riveted on what Tuấn said next.

"It's a love story!" Tuấn said. "With—can I say?—a twist. Beautiful woman, wife of powerful man. He was professor and friend and close associate of General Thiệu, commander of South Vietnamese armed forces *and* president of the puppet Saigon government."

"Yes," David said. "We often reported on him."

"Well," Tuấn said, obviously enjoying this, "the beautiful wife fell in love with a young American and he with her and they began a dangerous *'affaire d'amour.'*"

I sat frozen, looking out my window and pretending not to listen.

"Sounds like this will have an unhappy ending," David said.

"Not so!" Tuấn said. "Although the couple had many close calls, finally the professor was called to Saigon to serve the puppet government there and the young American finished his tour and went—who knows where?"

David, still clueless, said, "That doesn't sound like a happy ending. How does that relate to the 'good' in Mrs. Nữ's story?"

Quy jammed up close behind a fast-moving bus, blaring his horn and shaking his fist out the window. The bus kept rumbling but pulled onto the shoulder and Quy started to pass, blowing his horn now at an oncoming string of motorbikes. The motorbike riders veered off on the rough shoulder, bouncing like cowboys on bucking horses, and Quy roared unobstructed down the middle of the road.

"They're both about love!" Tuấn said. "Love can bloom in the midst of war. Think about it. Love for the land and poor people gave strength and courage to Mrs. Nữ, kept her strong even under torture. Love is what Richard felt when he saw Miss Nữ lie wounded, and love is what brought him back to search for her. Love is what the beautiful wife and the young American felt and risked their lives for, in spite of a jealous and dangerous man. And love probably brought you to Vietnam to be part of this quest."

David took a deep breath. "You are a wise man, Mr. Tuấn."

"You know," Tuấn said, "I've learned a lot in these past days from Richard and his writings, and Mrs. Nữ and her life."

"I'm sure I'll learn much today, too," David said.

"We all will."

Tuấn turned back to the front as we approached Quảng Trị. I sat still, fastened to the window and stunned by what I'd heard. *Tuấn knows everything about me and he's letting me know it. In a way it's not surprising – this is a Communist state – though this last revelation is shocking – but how does he know all this? Harder to understand is why he's not using it. He likes telling Annie and others about my "hearts and minds" time in Vietnam and ignoring the Chiêu Hội and combat time, at least up till now. What's going on here? And how long will it last?*

David's big elbow dug my ribs. "Did we lose you there?"

I looked away from the window but didn't say anything. I was lost in thoughts about Romy. *I saw her glowing beauty as the countryside passed, I heard her smokey, sexy voice as Tuấn and David talked. I called her Romy because she looked like a Vietnamese Romy Schneider, the German actress then one of the most beautiful women in the world. Oh Romy, the risks you took for our love, the risks we took for stolen moments together – and were the VC watching all the time?*

I glanced at Tuấn as he told David stories of his family.

If Miss Nữ—Mrs. Nữ—was the most remarkable (by far) human I'd met, Romy was the most vivacious, enchanting, and desirable. She was lit up with life, and I was obsessed with her from our first meeting at a cocktail party at the U.S. Consulate in Huế in early '66 to our last, under heavy duress, not long before the VC captured Huế in the attacks of Tết '68. Romy and the Ho Chi Minh Trail were my all-consuming passions in Vietnam, and both she and the land paid a price for that, adding, no doubt, to my karma. I persuaded her to be my French teacher, and we became lovers, head-over-heels, crazily, recklessly in love. Her husband was powerful, dangerous, jealous, suspicious, a gambler, partier, renowned in his field, and personally connected to the very top of the Saigon government. And ours was a "hopeless" love: no future, only an intense present. She knew—we knew—I would leave Vietnam some day, and she—devoted mother of four young children—would stay. "Devoted mother, unfaithful wife," she ruefully described herself in French. "Victim of a forbidden love."

We rumbled across a river bridge, with motor scooter riders hugging the sides to stay out of our way, and we entered Hải Lăng District, Annie's territory. *Oh, God, was it wrong to love Romy? And how could it have been otherwise? Was it wrong to help capture Annie? And how could it have been otherwise? I was on fire for life in the extreme, and ready — eager — to risk it all to get closer and closer to the source of the flames. And Tuấn, like God, knew it all.*

We rolled into what used to be Quảng Trị City and parked at the beginning of Annie's garden.

"You talk, I'll film," David said. "Here we go."

We approached the house. Quy stayed behind, shouting *Đi!* at the kids who were starting to gather. Annie stepped out of a small annex to the front of the house wiping her hands from rolling incense sticks.

"This is your friend?" she said, smiling.

"Yes, this is David."

They shook hands. The rest of the family gathered. I felt already in a strange dream-state.

"Let's go in and sit at the table," Annie said.

"We have gifts," I said, and David and I handed over the big bags.

"You," Annie smiled, "and they are welcome. Thank you for coming."

The daughters, the husband, and the kids gathered around the table. The husband gestured for us to sit. David set up his camera. The eldest daughter brought tea.

"You were making incense sticks?" I asked.

Annie smiled, almost shyly. "Yes, for the holidays." She gestured to the teenage girls. "We'll sell them at the marketplace."

"May we continue our conversation?" I asked. "And David will film us."

She smiled again. "Remember, I told you that you and he are welcome any time."

"Would you start where we left off? You were put into the vehicle, and—"

"Before I begin there, may I ask you a question? I've been thinking of it since you were here last."

I wondered what was coming and felt uneasy. "Yes, of course."

"Last time you said you felt bad when you saw I was captured. But you set out to capture me and you succeeded. Why did you feel bad?"

I felt the words begin to cascade out of me and I had to pause frequently for Tuấn to catch up with his translations.

"When I saw you flash across the path I was hiding beside, like a spirit, a ghost, something inside me changed. I didn't know what it was then, but it was with me as I chased you through the bamboo and when you jumped into the river. I started shooting ahead of you, trying to make you stop or turn back. When I saw you would not stop, a voice in my head shouted, 'Oh my God, you can't let her get away!' while another said, 'Oh my God, I'm going to kill her!' I saw my bullets hit all around your head. When you reached the other side and fell, I was sure I'd hit you. Then you jumped up and ran and I shot again with the same two voices screaming in my head, 'You can't let her get away!' and 'Oh, my God, I'm going to kill her.' I saw my bullets hit all around your flying feet and you dove forward into the darkness and disappeared. I was sure I had shot you in the back. I ran across the bridge afraid of what I would find. When I saw you lying on the ground with blood covering the side of your head, I was sure I had done it. I had killed the most remarkable human being I had ever seen. *I can't live with this*, I thought, and I wanted to walk away and shoot myself. Then I learned you were only wounded and it was a grenade that did it, not me. I felt so relieved. Then I started to wonder what would happen to you next."

"Can we take a break?" David asked. "I need to make some adjustments here."

"Yes," I said with a sigh of relief. "Let's take a break."

The girls refilled our tea glasses. The husband reached across the table and grasped my hand. His grip was warm and strong. Tuấn talked to David about his camera.

Annie gazed at me with a soulful look. "You had a heart for an enemy," she said.

"Yes," I said, looking into her eyes, "I guess I did."

The girls brought out some of our gifts to share, colorful fruits of many kinds. *I had a hard time imagining tough and scary Quy buying these. Maybe he just said, "Fill these bags."*

"These are some of our favorites," Annie said. "Thank you very much. The children love them, too. Shall we continue? I have one more question. You said something changed when you saw me run across the path. What changed?"

I thought about it. *I can't tell her I fell in love with her in that moment, or the dream I had of her that night, when we sat close and talked, and she looked like the beautiful Miss Moon of Huế. I'll try her tactic with Rang and her interrogators, partial truths leading in other directions.*

"From the sounds I heard from the house, I pictured you knocking the two Saigon soldiers aside and bursting through the walls of the house. Then you—or your spirit—crossed my path and began crashing through the bamboo to the river. You were like a wild animal, a deer, running to escape a tiger. And then diving, swimming with bullets all over you. Later when I thought about this, I compared you to the superheroes I worshiped as a young boy, great football players like the mighty Jim Brown, or actor-athletes like Johnny Weissmuller, the Olympic swimmer who played Tarzan in the movies. And you had the courage— maybe more—of Audie Murphy, the top U.S. hero in World War II. He was an actor, too, who played himself in the movie about his life."

Tuấn broke into his translation to say, "I saw his movie, *To Hell and Back!*"

Annie was still not satisfied. "But what changed?"

I'll give her a part of the truth, I thought.

"I began to think we could never win," I said. "Not if all the VC were like you. And on the way back to the church, when you were hanging beneath the pole like a captured lion or tiger, I tried to ask one of the Saigon soldiers how you could do all the things you did, and where did you get the courage?

"And he said, 'There are no women like that on this side.' May we take another break? The tea is delicious."

We all got up and stretched. David filmed. The husband grasped my hand again. I felt a brotherly love for him. Annie observed me closely.

"Your turn," I said as we sat down. "Please tell us what happened after you were captured."

"I will," she said, "after one more question. You told me what you felt when I was captured. Now is a long time after that.

Many years have passed, much life has been lived. We worked, married, raised families. Surely you forgot about such a faraway event."

With a trembling hand I took a sip of tea. Her medal certificate and her husband's, with Hồ Chí Minh's face, looked down from the wall.

"No, I didn't forget. I wrote your story in a long manuscript about my time in Vietnam. I taught about it in my classes on the history of the Vietnam War. I told my children your story as an example of courage and love of country and dedication to a cause, to purpose in life, and to love for the land."

The room was silent for a while after Tuấn's translation. Then she said, "May I suggest that if you write this book, it should not be about me, but rather Vietnamese women. In the war, you could find heroes everywhere, many of them women. And we women have a long tradition of fighting for our country. I do not consider myself special. I was only following tradition and doing my duty."

I looked at her across the magic table. "I will consider that."

After the first visit's time of her barely looking at me, now we smiled easily at each other; the husband, too, and all the family. Annie, as a mature woman now and having lived a difficult and harrowing life, still had a cuteness, a wonderful impishness. Physically, she had thick skin, unlined forehead, small hands, muscular arms, thin chest—and her daughters were beautiful at twenty-two, twenty, eighteen, and sixteen. Did she look then like they did now?

"I am ready to tell you now," she said. "I was at Hải Lăng District Headquarters for six days in a terrible place. They questioned me often, and beat me heavily with a stick. They wanted to know who helped me in the hamlet, who gave me food, who were the other VC there. I told them I didn't know.

They didn't believe me, of course, and beat me more and more. The dungeon was filthy and my ear became infected. I wanted to die and was not afraid to die. I would have killed myself if I could. My children have not heard this story.

"They sent me to higher and higher military prisons for more questions and beatings. I gave them false information, like about a small hospital in the jungle where I said I worked. They gave me electric shocks and made me drink soapy water with pepper mixed in. Finally they put me in the prison bunker. This was a hole lined with bricks and no toilet. It was 1.8 meters deep and 80 centimeters wide. You could stand only. Every day they threw some food down to me. Gradually the hole began to fill with my body wastes. They kept me there for thirty days."

I sat stunned and on the inside, sunk in gloom. *How much was I responsible for this hell she had suffered? Was it my crowing to Rang that sent her to these higher and higher levels of horrific inquisitions? And what would I have to pay for this?*

"Finally they gave up on me and sent me to regular Quảng Trị Military Prison. I was there for three years, till 1972, when the North Vietnamese Army crossed the DMZ and came down from the mountains to liberate Quảng Trị. The Saigon soldiers loaded us prisoners aboard trucks and made a dash for Huế. But the NVA ambushed our convoy, killed the soldiers, and freed us all.

"I went back to doing my old job, humanitarian and political work in the hamlets. My husband and I got married. We had met early in the war and agreed to be married when the country was free. Now that Quảng Trị was liberated, we felt it was time."

As Tuấn translated, Annie and her husband sat close, shoulders touching, and smiling, no doubt remembering twenty-three years back to when so many dreams for their country and themselves began to come true. Victory—which had seemed so far away—now began to happen.

"Now we have four daughters," Annie smiled. "No sons—but we have our son-in-law—and maybe more sons-in-law to come."

She reached out for her girls and hugged them, half-laughing and half-crying, as the grandchildren looked on wide-eyed.

Tuấn leaned over to me. "Maybe that's enough for today."

"I agree. You did a great job, Tuấn."

He smiled. "My brain is exhausted from so much translating. But my generation needs to hear these stories. *I* need to hear these stories."

I felt I loved Tuấn, too, I loved them all, I was flowing with love—and tears.

We all started to rise from the table.

"I want to get a few more shots inside," David said. "How about if I meet you in the garden?"

"Good idea!" I said. *I felt wiped like Tuấn, but with my nerves about to explode. I needed some garden time.*

I stepped outside while David engaged Tuấn, Annie, and her husband within. I walked under a young citrus tree and stood there feeling its soothing energy. Annie's eighteen-year-old and sixteen-year-old approached shyly and stepped under the overhanging, thorny branches and wind-dancing, glossy leaves.

Haltingly, the older said, "We study English in school. May we speak to you?"

"You don't study French?"

They giggled nervously and the younger said, "No, we like English. We like American music."

"Oh, good," I smiled. "Who do you like?"

They skipped that and began asking in tandem a series of questions, some of which they knew the answers to, for they'd seen the family pictures I showed to Annie and their dad, but the ones learned in a beginning conversation course: "Do you have wife? Do you have children? Where do you live? What do you do?"

As we talked, I thought, *Was Annie this beautiful, this flower-fresh at sixteen and eighteen? She was a poor, hard-working country girl and already at eighteen being taken to Hải Lăng for questioning. Her VC life began soon after, of living underground and going to the mountains on secret trails for training. Could these two do what she did? Could any of us? My two youngest—who I'd be seeing in just a few days, thank God—were the same age.*

And then it hit me, and I had to fight hard to keep from bursting into tears. *I almost killed their mother, and if God or my guardian angels hadn't made my bullets go around instead of into her head, and around her feet instead of into her back, these two pure and precious beings wouldn't be here now, nor would their two lovely sisters inside, and neither would my three awesome darlings. Oh, thank you, God for saving all our lives! And may we go on to pay back with love and good works!*

The girls ran out of questions. The Lao Wind rustled leaves. I wasn't ready to end the questions or the pleasure of their company.

"You didn't tell me your favorite music yet."

They looked at each other and laughed. The older said, "Elvis Presley. We know he's old, but he's new to us."

"I knew a Vietnamese who looked like Elvis," I said. "His name was Vinh. He was from Quảng Trị, too. He was a good singer and guitar player. And drummer!"

"Oh, will you introduce us?" the younger said.

I chuckled and said, "He would be old now, too. Maybe a grandfather."

"Aww," they both said.

David poked his head out the door. "They want you to come in. We're saying goodbye."

We sat at the table one more time. The husband made a short formal speech of thanks, good will, and the family's wishes for good things for our families, and peace between our countries.

David leaned over and said to me, "I think you ought to ask her if there's anything we can do for her and her family."

I asked, Tuấn translated, and I thought her answer surprised us all.

"You probably heard the news on the radio yesterday. Your President Bill Clinton announced the normalization of relations with Vietnam and that a U.S. Ambassador will be coming to Hanoi soon. Our government and business people are very happy about this. We want to be friends with America as we once were. My request to you is this. Rebuild the Quảng Trị Citadel. This beautiful castle with its moat was a precious part of our heritage. As Mr. Tuấn told you, B-52s bombed it to nothingness. Restore it as a sign of friendship and peace. Ask the new U.S. Ambassador to help."

I looked at David. He looked at me. "We'll do what we can," I said. "I was in our Foreign Service. I'll write to our ambassador."

"I know you are going out to Vinh Dinh Bac now," she said, "where I was captured. I cannot go, but my thoughts will be with you. Is there anything you would like to say before you go?"

I took a deep breath. In a way, the whole trip had been leading up to this moment. I ventured my hand across the table again and she took it in her warm strong hands. Barely able to speak, I looked into her eyes and forced the words out. "I'm very sorry for what we did to you and your country and I wish it never would have happened."

She squeezed my hand. "As you know, we Vietnamese believe strongly in destiny. Because of that war, we had a chance to meet. Thank you for coming here and many good wishes to your family. I hope we meet again."

We said our last goodbyes, passed through the garden, got in the mini-van, and were gone. My head was in a whirl, a high-energy vortex of swirling faces, feelings, words, touches.

David leaned forward and asked Tuấn, "Can we drive past where the Citadel was? This could be useful when we try to promote its restoration. Huế Citadel is being restored. Why not Quảng Trị?"

"Of course."

After the Citadel, soon we were in the countryside, driving the roads we took with the Love Team, the Ambush Team, and to capture and then transport Annie. Behind us, dust trailed from Quy's fast driving. Far beyond, the blue-haze mountains of the Ho Chi Minh Trail rose mysterious and alluring. Ahead, nearby but out of sight, the long, golden-sand beaches stretched, and the South China Sea glistened in mid-day summer sun. I loved this place, and it was almost time to say goodbye.

David shot out the window and often asked to stop as we passed water buffalo mired in mud, green paddies, thatched houses, kids.

"The light!" he said. "I'd forgotten the clarity of the light in the Vietnamese countryside. Oh, to have this light in LA!"

Ahead, the ruined church rose powerfully against the blue sky. We rumbled across the wooden bridge, parked, and got out. The barbed wire around the church was gone, but otherwise it looked the same. I half-expected to see the PF come out of their hideouts among the bushes and ruins, and the hard-faced PF sergeant sneeringly ask for "Captain Rose."

A woman in a conical hat came riding up on a bicycle and engaged Tuấn in lively conversation. He brought her quickly to David and me, while sullen Quy leaned against a pock-marked pillar smoking.

"You'll be amazed!" Tuấn said. "This woman is Thúy, Mrs.

Nữ's replacement. She's Chairperson of the Humanity Branch of the District Government here. This is how Mrs. Nữ did her job after Quảng Trị was liberated, on a bicycle!"

The two engaged in more fast conversation while David filmed. I questioned her about her work with the poor people of the district.

"Which is just about everyone," she said with a smile. "I've just come from there, Vinh Dinh Bac, where you're going." She pointed to the tree line across the rice fields. "You can't drive that vehicle there. You'll have to walk."

Quy growled, threw down his cigarette, and stomped on it.

Good, I thought. *We'll have to walk, just like that night.*

"Mrs. Nữ trained me," Thúy said. "The people of the district love her."

"Quy will stay here with the van," Tuấn said. "We three will hike to the hamlet. Richard will show us the route they took that night."

The bridge, the stream, dry grass underfoot, blue sky (not black), white clouds, dazzling light: I led as I had been led that Night of Wandering Souls, along the stream, then across the fields, and among the sandy grave mounds, where I visualized us being ambushed by Annie and her men, and our bodies twitching, our blood red on the salt-white sand.

We entered the tree line shading the hamlet path and suddenly encountered a mustachioed farmer in conical rice-straw hat leading a big water buffalo and heading toward the thatched houses ahead. Tuấn engaged him in fast conversation, told him what we were doing there, and he said in heavy country dialect, "You must come meet my wife. She's got a story for you!"

We passed trees, gardens, houses, spirit-houses, sheds, a buffalo shed, and the bridge where Rosie, "the strong man," carried Annie over. We came to the big mango tree where the betrayer sat and trembled at the coming of Annie, and the path going east toward the dunes and the sea where we laid among stinking dark shapes in the hamlet shitting place. The uncle's house that Annie ran from was gone, not even a foundation left, and I shivered for the fate of that old man and all the betrayer's family. We passed where Annie flashed like a ghost across the path and crashed like a deer through the bamboo and I followed, already in love with her, whipped by the bamboo, and rifle in hand.

I paused where the young APT and I laid in the bamboo and watched the house and felt her energy-wave go through us, and he said, "She's coming."

The buffalo man guided us off the path and into the rice-drying yard of a thatched house. He led his buffalo to a shed out back and shouted, "Đôi ơi !" "Hey, Đôi! Come out!"

"Wait till you meet Đôi," Tuấn said. "This is more destiny."

Briefly I thought how much Tuấn had got into this, and then a round-faced woman poked her head out the door, saw us, and disappeared back inside.

"Đôi!" the buffalo man shouted. "Don't be afraid. Come out. They've come from Mrs. Nữ's!"

She came out slowly and shyly approached. She looked in her forties of a hard-working life, but with a sweetness like Annie's. She was slightly plump, too, a rarity in the Vietnamese agricultural world. She studied us with quick, darting glances and mostly focused on the buffalo-man.

"My wife," he said, and he put his arm protectively and proudly around her. "She was Miss Nữ's helper, and she helped carry her to the church."

"Oh, my God," David said, "I have to film this."

"We'll talk over there." The husband pointed to a weathered table under a mango tree. "Đôi, bring tea."

We sat at the old wooden table. Đôi came out in a change of clothes, with tea in stained plastic glasses. She sat shyly, the focus of all our attention. David and I presented the last of our fruit, held back in the hope we'd meet someone connected to Annie.

Tuấn pulled two letters out of the slim briefcase he always had with him. "These are letters of commendation and appreciation Mrs. Nữ and her husband wrote when they knew we were going to Vinh Dinh Bac. They felt sure we would find you here."

Đôi read the letters, the husband's first and then Annie's. As she read, she smiled, glowed, and the years seemed to fall away from her. She was a pretty young woman again, playing her role in the great struggle.

"I love Mrs. Nữ!" she said, as she read the last of Annie's letter.

"Ask her to tell her story," David said to Tuấn, "and as much as possible where it happened."

"We'll go down to the river," Đôi said.

We took a narrow, beaten path through the bamboo. In the hot afternoon wind, the bamboo clacked and groaned.

"This light!" David enthused, filming as we walked. "This has to be some of the world's best light."

We came to the bank. A small woven-bamboo boat was there, nestled in the mud.

Đôi pointed across the stream. "Miss Nữ's tunnel was on the other side," she said. "See the banana grove? It was under that. The entrance was under water."

"Miss Nữ's tunnel entrance was under water?"

"Yes," Đôi confirmed. "So it couldn't be seen."

In a swirl of memories, I thought of kid-times exploring the creeks and rivers near my little town in Iowa, looking for the underwater tunnel-entrances of muskrats and beaver, and I imagined Annie diving, swimming underwater, going through her tunnel into what must have been a muddy, wet world, and staying there in darkness until night came again. *How did she do it?*

"My job," Đôi said, "was to signal her when it was safe to come out. I did it in my boat, that boat. The way we fish on this river is by knocking on the sides of our boat with a stick. When there were no soldiers in the hamlet, I would knock on my boat with a special rhythm. She would know and come out. I would have rice and dry clothes for her. On the night she was captured, the soldiers came in after dark and were very quiet. I was sad when she was captured, and afraid, too. But she never told them about me."

A small fish jumped and I looked across at the banana grove and pictured Annie there, underground and under the roots, hunched or lying and waiting for that tapping signal. I would go crazy in five minutes there. *How did she do it?*

"She thought something was wrong that night," Đôi said. "She heard a dog bark and was going to her other secret tunnel in the house of the uncle of her betrayer."

"That house is gone now," I said. "What happened to the people who lived there?"

Đôi looked at her husband.

"*Đi Saigon*," the husband said in a brusque voice. "They went to Saigon."

Tuấn explained. "'Went to Saigon' means—" He drew his hand across his throat.

"Oh," we both said.

"After Miss Nữ was wounded," Đôi said, "the Saigon soldiers—and there were Americans with them, including a black man—got me and Miss Xuân—she lived next to me—to carry her to the church. I was so afraid for her and for me. I thought, 'Maybe they will kill me.' But they sent me and Xuân away and took her to Hải Lăng. I trembled all the way home, knowing they would torture her. I went to Đà Nẵng to hide in the city. After two years, I knew she didn't tell about me and I came back here and got married."

"A good wife she is, too!" The buffalo man smiled, putting his arm around her shoulder.

We walked back to the mango tree and said our goodbyes. Đôi waved from the door with the bag of fruit and letters in her hand.

The husband shook our hands vigorously with both his hard, dirt-creased hands and said, "You should get the Americans to build a new bamboo bridge across the river here and name it Mrs. Nữ's Bridge!"

"How about Nữ and Đôi's Bridge?" I said.

"Even better!" he said, and he went off chuckling to his buffalo shed.

"What an amazing day!" David said. "Now I want to film you telling your story where it happened, where you shot at her in the water, and at the bridge."

We spent most of an emotional afternoon re-creating my role in the story, and it was almost dark when we got back to Huế. Nearing the Mimosa, while stopped at the river bridge, an oncoming bus lightly touched the side of the mini-van. It was hardly a scratch, but Quy flew into a rage, jumped back into the van, and began pursuing the bus, driving like a madman up and down narrow streets, blowing his horn constantly, his forearms twitching, and muttering curses in a continual stream. Pedestrians leaped for their lives out of our way and motorbike riders fled to sidewalks and into storefronts as Quy hurtled on, this way and that, trying to find the bus.

David and I looked at each other wide-eyed, expecting at any moment we were going to run over someone or smash into another vehicle. In the front, Tuấn sat silently, seemingly unperturbed or perhaps, though he was obviously Quy's boss, unwilling to confront him while he was in a killer rage. *Or maybe, I thought, this is just the way the police operate.*

Suddenly, the bus appeared ahead of us and Quy zoomed around it, cut it off, jumped out, and stormed aboard. The next thing I expected to see was the driver's lifeless body flying out the door, but what we heard was Quy screaming curses and I visualized the driver and passengers frozen in terror.

Quy came out, muttering Vietnam's worst curse, got in, slammed the door, and drove us to the Mimosa.

Over the next few days, we went on more searches for former enemies and adventures with Tuấn, thank God with a different driver, an older man who for several years drove Russian-made trucks on the Ho Chi Minh Trail and regaled us with stories of life on the Trail, American air attacks, and one story that got us all, especially, Tuấn, laughing.

"Some NVA soldiers, country boys fresh from the North, found mysterious cans that had fallen from a U.S. helicopter. When they opened them, the cans began fizzing wildly and the NVA, thinking they were a fiendish American booby trap, screamed, ran, and dove for cover, while their older comrades watched and laughed uproariously. They were, in fact, cans of warm soda pop! Those county boys had never seen that before!"

We visited Ái Tử, where the huge U.S. Quảng Trị Combat Base had sprawled, and a VC cemetery now contained the remains of hundreds of "heroes." I was wounded here outside the wire, and thought I was killed and came back to life as a different (or changed) person, and where I said goodbye to the warrior life. Water buffalo grazed peacefully among the grave mounds now, and a thorny poppy-like flower bloomed, pure white with a yellow center.

We rode with Tuấn up to Bạch Mã, "White Horse," Vietnam's

newest national park, where the Vietnamese emperor and his
French masters had villas in the cool mountain forest, which I
flew over in '66 in a blue and white CIA Air America helicopter
and took pictures of because we had intel the VC were having a
high-level meeting there. On the way up, we stopped at a road-
builders camp and Tuấn played the guitar while a road builder
sang a song I remembered from the Love Team nights sung by
Chinh, the young disabled singer, and I was swept again by tear-
rushes. We met another "thổ công," an "Earth-god" like Việt, Long,
a forest ranger who could imitate the songs of thirty bird species,
and who called birds to the roadside for us to see, and climbed
tall trees agile as a monkey to bring down wild, magical fruit for
us. We saw three jungle-cat kittens drinking from a stream, heard
gibbons, a bear, and an eerie, loud, and penetrating insect song
that took me back to missions on the Ho Chi Minh Trail. For old
time's sake, I took a short solo hike into the jungle and in spite of
stuffing my pants into my socks, came back with leeches sucking
blood from my legs. We saw villas bombed to nothingness like
Quảng Trị Citadel, and heard plans for this to become a major
eco-tourist destination.

We went to Cổ Luỹ, except for a new bridge looking unchanged
from when the Love Team performed at the church ruins. We met
a tall, ex-guerilla in an NVA pith helmet on the hamlet path who
said, "You have to meet my colonel!" and escorted us to a small,
neat house beside the river. We spent an amazing two hours with
Colonel Miễn, white-haired, short, fit, strong, dynamic, bright-
eyed, and with an unlined face and erect posture that gave no
hint of his eighty-five years or his life as a warrior fighting first
the Japanese when they occupied Vietnam in World War II, then
the French when they tried to regain their control after the war,
then us and the South Vietnamese. He brought out a shoebox
filled with his medals and covered his kitchen table with them

as we drank tea and talked, and David filmed it all. Col. Miễn rose to command all VC forces in Quảng Trị and Huế and he did it from an underground bunker here in Cổ Luỹ, his home hamlet, and from a secret house in Huế. We met his wife, who was also in the struggle and who listened to him admiringly, and his son, a dark haired, strong, and fit copy of him, who fought the Khmer Rouge in Cambodia and the Chinese on Vietnam's northern border. "The Chinese were easy to kill," the son said with a grin, "and we killed many."

I asked about the guerrilla leader Võ Công Đỗ and the tall ex-guerrilla answered, "Dead, killed by a mine in 1971."

On the medal-covered kitchen table, Tuấn pointed out two with Ho Chi Minh's face in profile. "These are Vietnam's highest medals," he said, "like your Congressional Medal of Honor. And he has *two* of them. Maybe the only person ever. It's the Presidential Medal."

"General Giáp himself gave me this one!" Miễn said. "Look!"

On the wall in the small living room was a framed black and white picture of General Võ Nguyên Giáp, generally considered the mastermind of victory against both the French and the Americans, pinning a medal on young Miễn's chest.

"In the war against the French," Miễn said. "Here, I give you one."

He slid one to me, and when I tried to refuse he smiled and said, "No, no, you take it. I still got one!"

"Take it," Tuấn said. "It's a very special gift."

Suddenly I realized, as I looked into Miễn's bright eyes, that this was the man who allowed me to live for three years of my life. As commander in Huế and Quảng Trị for the years I lived there, he could have ordered my assassination at any time. Easy: knock on my door in Huế where I had no guard on my house or wait for me to drive out of my compound in Quảng Trị. I loved this man!

Miễn told how, when the Marine CAP team moved into Cổ Luỹ, the VC found ways to keep things quiet. And they appreciated the help the Marines gave the people. Then he got a sad look, and he nudged the tall ex-guerrilla. "We didn't want to kill Nhieu and Joe. But they were in the wrong place at the wrong time." *This obviously happened after I had left Quảng Trị, and I wondered if Slater, Doc Johnson, and the others were still there then.*

We said goodbye with handshakes and hugs. The tall ex-guerrilla held onto my hand with his big, strong, and calloused farmer's hands as if he didn't want me to leave. He and I had tears in our eyes. *I felt I was learning every day about love between former enemies, now come together in peace.*

We drove the narrow dike road out of Cổ Luỹ and stopped where it met the old Street Without Joy. David wanted to film back toward the hamlet, the Lâm Thủy Forest, and the mountains beyond. As he shifted his camera to the east, the dunes, and the sea, and I began thinking about home, we heard a rhythmic "thump-thump-thump" coming from behind us. A one-legged, middle-aged man on crutches was coming toward us as fast as he could, and I thought, *Sướng! The VC whose leg was cut off in the Quảng Trị Hospital after the night ambush in the dunes. Could it be him?* This trip kept turning up memories, and I felt again Sướng's weight and body heat on my back as we trudged through the sand, and the bump-bump-bump of his balls against the base of my spine.

It was not Sướng. There were a lot of missing-limbs people in Vietnam. The man breathlessly told his story to Tuấn, who translated it to us.

"He says he was in the ARVN 1ˢᵗ Division. He lost his leg fighting the VC. He wants to go to America. Some of his family made it there. He's applied for an exit visa. He wants you to help him get it."

David and I looked at each other.

Tuấn came to the rescue. "I'll get his name and enquire in Huế about it. These things take a long time. Many people want to go."

Finally it was time for the last trip to Phú Bài Airport and goodbye to Huế, to the Mimosa "family," Hoàng and Liên, and to Tuấn, who came to the airport with us (maybe to make sure we were going). Tuấn, who I once feared was taking me for my last ride, had become like a brother, and I found it hard to choke out the words of how special the trip was for me and how important was his role in it.

His voice, too, cracked with emotion. "From the MIA missions and guiding other veterans, I know how you feel. At another goodbye here, I made a big mistake. I asked a veteran who had lost his leg here—we had become friends like you and David have become to me—and I asked him something I will never ask again—'How many people did you kill?' And he looked at me and said simply, 'I didn't come here to find my leg.' Then he was gone. For a long time I puzzled over that. Finally, I thought I knew—whatever happens, we have to go on. Mrs. Nữ said something like that, too. I will always remember you and David and the time we shared. I wish the best for you and your families."

We boarded the plane, the engines revved, and the props turned. The song on the intercom as we rolled was "Love Changes Everything." We flew through cloud-mountains back to Saigon, my eyes filled with tears almost all the way.

David came with me to film the last visit to Má's house. She looked older than just two weeks ago. Did I, too? We greeted each other in the usual way.

She gripped my hands, smiled, and said, "*Toujours beau*. Still handsome."

I squeezed back and said, "*Toujours belle*. Still beautiful."

We sat and held hands. David panned up the wall to a 1927 picture of her looking much like her four daughters. Four daughters: like Annie and her husband.

I said in Vietnamese, "I love you a lot, Má."

She smiled and said in Vietnamese, "Má also loves you a lot." Then she switched to French. "Tell me how you feel about Thúy-Minh now."

"I love her like a sister, a special friend. Her new husband, too. We all became friends on Guam when she and Lani were refugees there. They're very happy in Texas. Her house is big and beautiful."

She patted my hands. "Yes, I've seen pictures. You know you'll always be part of our family."

"That means a lot to me, Má."

"We waited a long time to say it."

"I've always felt it, even though Thúy-Minh and I parted. I'm sorry about all that, Má. I'm sorry I hurt her and all of you."

She released my hands and spread hers. "It's destiny. We have to accept it."

David and I went back to our guest house, once the home of General William Westmoreland when he commanded all U.S. forces in Vietnam. How strange it felt to be here now on this kind of mission. For me, one more night in Saigon; David would stay another week. Most of my thoughts now were of Hawaii, family, and home.

After dinner, I fell asleep quickly for the first time on the trip. At 3 a.m. I awoke with a start, again with the feeling of someone—or something—in the room with me. Then I realized the "presence" was three words deeply etched, glowing, and pulsating like living beings in my mind: "Peace-Healing-Reconciliation." Four words connected to these came into my

mind: "Nature-Family-Former Enemies." Now with these seven
words like living, illuminated presences inside my head, I saw
the trip in a new light, not so much to gather material for a book,
but as an opportunity to sit with Annie and Má at their tables,
to hold and be held by their hands, to say and to hear words
that needed to be spoken, and to see the pure land, the sea, and
the sky, to remember my love for them, and see how they had
recovered from the beating I and we gave them. "Peace-Healing-
Reconciliation: Nature-Family-Former Enemies." This is why I
came back to Vietnam. "Love changes everything."

I stayed awake thinking about this till it was time to get up
and go home.

EPILOGUE

...never will I forget you...

—Hoàng Thị Nữ

AFTER I RETURNED to Hawaii, I wrote to the new U.S. ambassador in Hanoi to ask about the restoration of Quảng Trị Citadel, as Annie had requested. I was surprised to learn that as part of the normalization of relations, the U.S. Congress had included the stipulation that no financial liability could be laid at America's door for damage done in the Vietnam War. If the Citadel was to be restored, some other entity would have to do it.

Writing this now in a new century (in 2022), I am happy to report that this precious historical relic *has* been restored (by the People's Committee of Quảng Trị Province), and includes a park, museum, memorial to the eighty-one day battle here in 1972, bell tower, and nine-ton bell, which is rung on holidays and full-moon days (like the Day — and Night — of Wandering Souls). One of the holidays with a special connection to the Citadel is War Invalids and Martyrs Day (a kind of combination Memorial Day and Veterans Day) on July 27. In addition to the bell-ringing, this holiday, to commemorate those injured and lost in the war, is celebrated by people releasing small rafts packed with flowers, candles, and incense sticks on the Thạch Hãn River, which flows along the Citadel park's border. Annie was rolling incense sticks on our second visit in mid-July, no doubt preparing for this holiday. Rafts of flowers, candles, and burning incense sticks, launched and floating down the broad and beautiful Thạch Hãn as the bell from the Citadel tolls: "No man is an island, entire of itself; every man is a piece of the continent, a part of the main... Any man's death diminishes me because I am involved in mankind; therefore never send to know for whom the bell tolls; it tolls for thee..."[3]

In teaching my college students about the Vietnam War and its aftermath and connections, I noted the trip had added new dimensions and complexities related to the people I had met, the stories heard, the political situation felt, and the land observed. Families separated, decimated, and lost on both sides during the years of heavy combat and in the "boat people" disaster after, were among the great tragedies of the war, but families were still one of the great strengths (and joys) of Vietnam. The U.S. entry into the war was as complex for geopolitical, historical, military, and cultural reasons, as mine was simple for personal and psychological (I wanted to experience it). Some of the motivations and actions, both and national and individual, could be seen as "noble" (wanting to help anti-communist South Vietnamese resist a communist takeover, preventing a "domino effect" in Asia, refugee assistance, rural development, Cold War rivalries and struggle), and some were not. Both sides committed immense harm to mostly-rural people (and the land). War is the Devil's playground. Finally, the war proved to be unwinnable by us, though it took eight long years of heavy combat for that lesson to be learned. Among the best takeaways from the trip, that also became part of my classes, were the genuine joy many Vietnamese, official and private, expressed at the news of the normalization of relations with the U.S., the resilience and healing of nature, the hugs and tears with former enemies, and, of course, holding Annie's and Má's hands and receiving their

---

3   John Donne, Meditation 17, *Devotions upon Emergent Occasions*, 1624.

smiles and blessings. It all felt like love, like redemption.

I also wrote to Annie, and below is her reply, translated from Vietnamese.

June 10, 1996
Dear Mr. Richard Stevens,
I received your letter more than half a year ago, but never got a chance to respond to you. That has been bothering me. However, I do hope you'll understand and ignore the time to "enjoy" my letter now!

According to me, time is not important. It's not something you and I can use to blame each other for. It is the heart that counts. Our Vietnamese famous writer, Nguyễn Du, in *The Tale of Kiều*, wrote, "The heart is worth three times more than the talent." You are American, yet you do have the heart. You are so far away, with time, everything stays in the past. In other words, the war has separated hundreds of families, children from their fathers and wives from their husbands. At the same time, thousands of people sacrifice their lives for their country's independence and freedom. I am a Vietnamese woman, born and raised in that spirit. As I remember, when my secret cave was discovered, armed soldiers surrounded me and gunshots were all over me. Yet I don't understand why I have survived until now. Maybe, as you said, "everything is God's will." That's also why we were able to see each other again. After more than twenty-five years, you still have the heart to visit an enemy! In a war, there will always be winners and losers. However, I always respect you for your love of human beings. Time to weep over our losses has gone. What's now important is the present. That's why you don't hold grudges for the past, for what happened more than one fourth of a century ago. And, the bottom line, if you have a love for your fellow humans, you will always feel the closeness of hearts no matter how far away we are from each other.

After your visit to Vietnam, you've left us with love and compassion. You admire our country and our people. To tell you the truth, the Vietnamese are very enduring and hard-working. Vietnamese women, particularly, are always devoted and loyal to their families and their works. That's why, to me, my courage and loyalty are just part of being a Vietnamese woman. It's not noble, it's just normal, if not trivial. In Vietnam, during the war, you could see heroes everywhere. And thanks to that war, you and I had a chance to meet with each other.

Have you achieved your dream? Has your book been published? I am not sure if the main character is myself. Very humbly, let me introduce you the Vietnamese woman, whom beloved Uncle Hồ has called "heroic, courageous, loyal, and defiant." Inherited from heroic blood of the Trung sisters and Lady Triệu, the Vietnamese women consider fighting against foreign invasion natural and normal.

The time I met you and received your letter has been in the past, but never will I forget you with your caring love of our family. Please accept our gratitude and also give our best regards to your family. I hope you don't mind my mistakes in this letter. That's what it means to have a human heart!

I wish you health, luck, and success in everything. And of course, like you, I am looking forward to hearing from you.

Affectionately,
Hoàng Thi Nữ

ACKNOWLEDGMENTS

A big Hawaiian *aloha* and *mahalo* ("love and thanks") to all who appear in this book. Whether in large or small roles, you all played an important part, and hopefully I brought you alive in these pages as you once lived and breathed in "real life."

Special thanks to my buddy Jerry Miki, who *insisted* I go back to Vietnam to search for Annie, and whose generosity made it possible. In the same vein, Lê Quang Tuấn in Vietnam made it possible to actually *find* Annie, and he became a brother on our many adventures together.

David Oyster, documentary filmmaker *extraordinaire*, not only captured our amazing time together on film, and the awesome people and nature of Vietnam, but he enhanced it all with his erudite and genial presence. Thanks, David, for the Father's Day call that set it all in motion.

Thúy-Minh's family, led by wonderful, "*toujours belle*" ("still beautiful") Má, opened doors for me (literally) from my arrival at Ho Chi Minh City's Airport to lodging and contacts in Huế, and most of all, to the heart of the family itself.

John Donne's "No man is an island; entire of itself" is powerfully true of authoring a book, and the work is reaching a wider world because of the caring professionalism, compassion, and contacts of my brilliant literary agent and friend, Arnie Kotler, who, in a long career of editing, publishing, advising, and acting as agent, has brought a vast catalog of valuable and inspirational books and articles into being. *Mahalo*, Arnie: your belief in this project has turned dream into reality.

Maxine Hong Kingston, author of the classic *The Woman Warrior*: many thanks for pointing the way to Arnie, for your work for peace, and for being an inspiration and model to so many of us aspiring writers. Thank you seeing, in your reading of Mrs. Nữ's letter, the importance of sharing her story. Your urging to tell it in its fullness helped push the book to completion.

This book was written, first as part of the 2,000-page manuscript mentioned in Chapter 5, and then standing alone, over an astonishing period of *fifty-three years*, from Annie's capture in 1969 that I recorded the details of on cassette tapes immediately after the event, to the last additions and revisions suggested by my astute publisher, Graham Earnshaw, in 2022, which took the story to higher, deeper, and wider levels. Another *aloha* and a *mahalo nui* ("big thanks") to Graham for his value-laden contributions.

Ivy Doan, Vietnamese college student in China and intern at Earnshaw Publishing, with the knowledge of her native language and familiarity with the stories of Vietnam's women warriors, added greatly to the authenticity of the manuscript. *Mahalo*, Ivy!

In the long period of the gestation of the book, while life was being lived on three continents (Asia, Europe, and North America) and three islands (Guam, St. Vincent, and Hawaii Island), up many mountains and into many valleys, three magnificent and magnanimous women, my wives—Thúy-Minh Stevens Starkey, Mercédes Menor Fernandez Stevens, and Angelica Ku'ulei-Fowler Stevens—typed and retyped the manuscript, and provided incisive editorial comment on the storytelling itself, and the life and motivations of Annie. I literally (physically) could not have done this without their dedication and help.

My children, Lani-Minh, Maria Cybele, and Daniel Thoreau, all about the same age as Annie's daughters, by being interested in the stories of her exploits, helped keep the book project alive.

(It was also an opportunity for them to learn about the American Annie Oakley, another great story.)

Finally, thanks to the subject of the book herself: Hoàng Thị Nữ (and her beautiful, welcoming family). My words fall short when trying to express all I learned from you, and felt about you, since that fateful meeting on the full-moon Night of Wandering Souls, so I will turn to a Hawaiian saying that in some way, I believe, says it all about the intertwining of lives and the journey of life itself: "*Aloha ke Akua*": "God is love."

About the Author

Richard Stevens grew up in Prairie City, Iowa, and joined the Marines soon after high school, mostly for adventure. He later became a Refugee Advisor for the U.S. Agency for International Development and a Foreign Service Officer. He served in Vietnam for three years in both military and civilian roles, was wounded twice, went missing once, and received several Vietnamese medals and the Purple Heart. In a "treetop revelation" on a reconnaissance mission, he realized the U.S. was fighting against nature and would lose, and the VC were working with nature and would win, and that there were lessons here worldwide. Returning to school, he wrote two books on organic gardening in Hawaii, and two on the Ho Chi Minh Trail and the role of nature in the Vietnam War. He has taught for over thirty years, and has received numerous awards for teaching, native tree planting, and ancient trail restoration, including the Dr. Richard Linn Stevens Endowed Scholarship for Restoration, and a National "Take Pride in America" Award from the U.S. Department of the Interior. He lives on an agroforestry farm in Hawaii.

Printed in the USA
CPSIA information can be obtained
at www.ICGtesting.com
LVHW031054090823
754733LV00003B/91